Sharon Browman,
614 Westlake Ave.,
484-0146.

FIRST FLOWERING

Published Works of Anthony Frisch

THOUGH I SPEAK Poems, 1949
THE HOUSE Poems, 1950
THIRD POEMS, 1951
STEINE AUS KANADA, Vienna, 1953
POEMS, 1954

FIRST FLOWERING

A Selection of Prose and Poetry
By the Youth of Canada

ANTHONY FRISCH
Editor

JOHN HARASTI
Assistant Editor

TORONTO
KINGSWOOD HOUSE
1068 BROADVIEW AVENUE

Published by
KINGSWOOD HOUSE
1068 Broadview Avenue, Toronto, Canada

First Edition,
June, 1956

Printed and bound in Canada by
THE BRYANT PRESS, TORONTO

This book is set in 11 on 13 point Fairfield type

HOW THIS BOOK CAME TO BE

No Editor's comments could add or detract from the merits of a book such as this. I believe it is the first national anthology of High School Prose and Poetry ever attempted. And I think this book is a miracle; less because the stories and poems were written by young people in a young land, supposedly without literary traditions and interests; but a miracle because it was possible for me to give reality to what had been an idea less than a year ago.

As a writer, and particularly a poet, I had known what we in our craft and sullen art know, that the gift of words is lodged within more people than become authors.

Last year then, when I confronted my Grades IX, X and XII students at Pickering College, to teach them English, I could not believe that these thirteen- to eighteen-year-old non-verbal, down-to-earth Canadians had been constructed differently by their Creator than any other similar group of young people anywhere on the globe. Surely, they had a sense of wonder! And, surely, they could put down on paper what sufficiently spoke to their condition, as Friends put it, if only I could tap their enthusiasm and kindle their natural taste and intelligence!

And so they began to write. Much of it, most of it, the world would consider pretty bad. But, at least, what was written, was written. And it was their own. They wrote much that year and some of it was not bad at all. Some of it was very good indeed.

So I reasoned: if this could be done, and was being done in my classes, surely this was being done in many classrooms from coast to coast! And if that was so, why not show it to the world?

Last summer, I cancelled a trip to Europe, took a room in Toronto and started telephoning publishers. Were they interested in publishing a collection such as this one? They were not interested. In a sense I cannot blame them, because publishing in

Canada is a risky business, and to sink money into a first book of its kind makes anybody think twice. Only the Publishers of the book took a chance.

While negotiations with the publishers dragged on, I wrote about my idea to the Provincial Deputy Ministers of Education, and to the Deputy Minister of the Federal Department of Northern Affairs, which administers the Yukon and North West Territories. To my great surprise they all replied enthusiastically. Then, 7000 posters in English and French, asking for contributions from students, were printed and sent to all Canadian High Schools. The Canadian Press and the Canadian Broadcasting Corporation spread the word. It was taken up, editorially or otherwise, by almost every newspaper in Canada. By the middle of January, John Harasti and I had waded through the 5300 contributions received, and this book contains what could be accommodated. And what is written, is written.

Anthony Frisch

Newmarket,
May, 1956

CONTENTS

ACKNOWLEDGMENT OF THANKS

I hope the authors whose work could not be used will not be too disappointed. I should like to thank every one of them for making this Anthology possible.

I should like to thank the Deputy Minister and Mr. Siveritz of the Department of Northern Affairs; the Deputy Ministers and officials of all Provincial Departments of Education; the Chairman of the Canadian Broadcasting Corporation; Mr. Charles Bruce, General Superintendent of the Canadian Press; Professor B. C. Diltz of the Ontario College of Education; Harry Beer and Don Stewart; the Principals of Secondary Schools and English teachers from coast to coast; the city editors and editorial writers of most Canadian newspapers; Dunc Cameron; Clem Beauchamp; and my Grades X and XII students who enjoyed reading Anthology submissions more than any text they had ever used.

ANTHONY FRISCH

CURRICULUM DEPARTMENT

Sharon -

Many thanks — a thoroughly enjoyable experience.

Remarkable sensitivity and facility with words on the part of so many!

Thanks for sharing

Mary

MISS MARY MATHEWS
Reading Consultant

L'AURORE DE PIERRE

Il ventait très fort ce jour-là.

De gros nuages, troués de petites plaques d'azur très rares, couraient dans le ciel, se bousculaient, envahissants. Dans la ruelle où la fenêtre de sa petite chambre obscure donnait, Pierrot regardait, assis sur son vieux lit étroit et boîteux, cette partie du monde semblable au tout, où il vivait.

Une flaque d'eau boueuse qui n'avait jamais le temps de s'évaporer entre deux pluies, croupissait sur les bords du trottoir, près d'une poubelle pleine d'ordures immondes, renversées, vomissures . . .

Un tourbillon leva de terre des morceaux de journaux crasseux et un nuage lourd, épais de poussière grise, vint lécher le bord de sa fenêtre . . .

Un mendiant en lambeaux, plus gris que la ruelle, passa; lui aussi vivait. Pour quoi? Pour qui?

Soudain, le soleil perça entre deux gros nuages et remplit, inonda la ruelle. Le mendiant resplendissait comme un temple abritant la gloire. La flaque d'eau était devenue un petit lac d'azur miroitant. Dans la chambre de Pierrot, un rayon de lumière partait — ou revenait, il ne savait trop — de la fenêtre et éclairait son crucifix sur le mur opposé. Dans ce brasier cylindrique, brillaient des milliers de petits diamants qui illuminaient toute la pièce . . . et alors Pierre comprit.

Tout est beau; il suffit de regarder de près . . . et avec amour, beaucoup d'amour. Tout est beau et utile et raisonné . . . sinon raisonnable.

Pourtant toujours, dehors, il ventait très fort ce jour-là. . . .

MARC JONCAS,
Québec

SUKANEN

It is an old man who sits on the steps of his cabin looking over his valley in the hush hour of twilight. The crocuses of spring softly close their petals, and the slough rings with the chirping of the frogs, and overhead little birds fly silently in the greyness of the evening sky. And from the arid hinterland comes the throbbing song of night.

It is an old face that scans with cool, pale eyes the tranquil scene: a face of age and sadness and great strength. The old man and his valley are silent and at peace, now, as the shadows darken and the prairie sleeps; yet, both are virgin and vital in the soul.

Sukanen . . . strange old man . . . sad old man . . . "that crazy Sukanen" . . . "that mad old Finn," they call him. Many stories are told of him in the community. He is said to have walked here to the Gopher Hill district from Wisconsin in the dead of winter many years ago; and his feet had frozen on the way. They say he had a wife in Milwaukee and that she had gone insane and had been sent to an asylum and their children had been sent to a home. They say, in winter he sleeps in a dog house, so that he will save fuel, keeping warm by the heat of his own body. The fat Nordic farmwives sit over steaming coffee and tell many stories of old Sukanen.

Of what do you think, old man who sits and views the night prairie? Of the sad life? Of the toil? Do not think of the tears, old man. But Sukanen does not really see the valley in this northern desert. He sees his little village on the lake near Tampere. He thinks he will build a boat and sail back to Finland, where he can die in peace in the land of his youth.

And they laugh, when they hear of it, in the barber shop and the kitchens; and in the general store they joke about it — they look down towards the muddy little river that creeps over the prairie to the yellow lake a few miles away. And they shake their heads and they laugh.

But Sukanen begins to build his boat. In the mist of the autumn morning the figure mounts the hill where he builds a little forge shop. He writes back east for sheets of iron; he hauls them from the station back to his valley. What a strange old man, they say. But he has saved enough money these many years to be able to stop wheat farming. Now he builds his boat.

The industry of the old man! With the power inherent in his race, he moulds the iron into a great machine, his own steam boiler. He is a great inventor, Sukanen.

Sometimes young girls bring him fresh coffee bread from their mothers. At recess, they sit in the shade behind the school and tell of his wonders. He has made a cover for his good, white teeth, to protect them from the fragments of metal that fly from the blows of his hammer upon the iron. And on the ceiling of his cabin he has drawn a beautiful design with black pencil. He has made a violin, himself, and a knitting machine. It is almost unreal, they say.

The metal ark is silhouetted against the red summer sky on the rocky hill above the droughted prairie. It is two years now. The old man will never finish it, they say. He might die soon. Uncle Svende says he is past eighty now.

What thing is it that grows within a man such as he — a seed of ardour, that is nurtured in the memory of pain, that grows until it dominates the soul? Does he say to himself: there can be no peace until this mission is completed?

And the work is slow. The winter falls. The dunes of snow roll over the prairies. And the valley of Sukanen is isolated in the shadows of the snow. When spring comes, the neighbours see that the winter has been hard on the old man. They think back to the days when he was active in the district, when he helped to build the Finn hall. But now he seems bitter. And the only world he cares for is that within his valley and his dreams. But his money is running out. "Can he pay the taxes?" they ask. All he has left are his horses, the herd that roams the valley of Sukanen unmolested and wild. And they are all he has to eat, as he works on his boat.

With the hunger, with the labour, has come also the spirit of malice. He has told his neighbours how he will move the boat down to the Saskatchewan river, he will follow it to the northern sea, and then to Finland. But they do not believe him. They joke with him. It hurts him that he is alone in his animity. But he must not be moved by them, by his loneliness—he must build his boat.

The next few years are hard on everyone and many leave the district; and people cannot wonder and worry about crazy old Sukanen in his valley. But in time stories come. . . .

He has almost finished his boat, now. It must be moved to the river. His valley is over-grown. His horses have all been killed. But he is filled with a great enthusiasm. He is near accomplishment! Once again, he goes to visit his neighbours, for the first time in many years; and he borrows a team.

At last, at last! The boat is on the river. He will live in the boat until it is finished. And he works and works. The iron hulk slowly sinks into the yellow mud. Another winter. There is no food. And he works and works.

The story drifts back to the old district that, in time, some mounties came down to the river bank and took Sukanen away from his boat. Many say he died at the Mental Hospital at Weyburn; but we like to believe the other story: that Sukanen has returned to his village on the lake near Tampere.

W. ROGER HARDING,
British Columbia

MY GRANDPA

My Grandpa was an Englishman,
He died at ninety-one,
And when he died, my Grandma cried,
She said "his days are done."

My aunt said, "it's a blessing
Because he is quite old,
But all the same his days on earth
Were valuable as gold."

Grace Pike,
Newfoundland

STAR GAZING

On a fluffy baby cloud drifting far above earth amid the deep blue and gold of the evening sky, a cherub was perched. It was an unusual sight to see him still, even for one fleeting moment of eternity, and not only was he still, but he was thinking deep and important thoughts. You see, he had almost reached the age when he would stop being a cherub and would find himself an angel — weren't his wing-tips already twenty-six inches from the ground? — and the thought had come to him that it was high time he decided upon his angelic career. He gazed at the stars around him as if they might furnish him with some divine inspiration, but instead of helping, they only chuckled and sent silvery beams frolicking towards him.

Perhaps he ought to be a halosmith, for he knew that with the recent increase in the number of angels he would certainly be needed. Should he present himself to the Master Halosmith (the one who, as an earth child, had been called Michelangelo) and become his apprentice? He thought of the delicate tracery and golden beauty which he would create — far, far more wonderful than anything that had ever been made — and his own halo quivered in his excitement. Then he remembered the snowseraphs that he and the other cherubs often made and the golden castles they built from stray sunbeams with roofs made of indignant stars. They had not always been beautiful for somehow the proportions were never completely accurate and one of the best statues had had a distinctly lop-sided appearance. No, the little cherub uttered a pensive sigh and decided that surely his talent must be needed elsewhere.

What could a young and not very wise angel do? It was no heavenly use sitting dreaming on the cloud if he couldn't come to any conclusion. Dreaming—perhaps that was it—he could create dreams! A tinkling laugh echoed over the firmament as he thought of the fun he would have chasing rainbows and then, breathless and triumphant, returning to the celestial workshop with his hands full of colourful visions. Perhaps, if he became exceptionally adept at his work he might be allowed to accompany the guardian angels on their flights and slip a tinted dream beneath some little earth-child's pillow.

Then, just as he had almost made up his mind completely, he had the most magnificent idea. He would be the angel who scattered stars into people's hearts! The lonely and uncertain would become gay and life-loving, the cruel would become gentle and merciful, and the hopeless would suddenly see a ray of happiness. If unenlightened mortals wondered where musicians found their tunes, or authors their stories, they would turn to him for their answer—to HIM!

Never in all his short life had the cherub felt such burning ecstasy as throbbed into his heart at this minute. Could anything be more rewarding than to know that you were creating gladness and beauty in men's hearts! As the cherub turned joyfully towards the Celestial City, he gave one final glance to the stars which had sent him this glorious message, and in his heart was a deep prayer of gratitude.

HANDA BRAY,
Quebec

WINTER ROAD

Sadly,
forsaken,
the white winter road
wanders away
into the dim distance,
bleak,
wind-swept,
unused.
Its solitary company
only
dwindling poles,
arms outstretched,
white hatted,
marching
single file
along its drifted ditches.

Allan Petrie,
Saskatchewan

THE SUNDANCE

The Sundance has been known to the Indians long before the outlaws came into our country, and to this day the Sundance is still known to the present Indians, but not as strong as it used to be.

The main reason we have the Sundance is to be happy and to pray.

The most important character of the Sundance is the Medicine Lodge Woman. She is the person who gives the date when we are to have the Sundance. It is held about two or three weeks, depending upon the important persons of each society being there to join their group.

The last four days and nights of the Sundance, the Medicine Lodge Woman stays in her tepee without eating or drinking anything, except early in the morning before the sun rises, when she gets a little to eat and some water to rinse her mouth with. Then she goes out for some fresh air.

On the fourth day, when the Medicine Log is to be chopped, she goes out anytime when the Horn's Society and Women's Society are ready to go down to the river to chop the log. She sits outside her tepee and waits for the log until it arrives. When it is brought back to the Sundance, the Horn's Society puts it up, with branches around it to cover the lodge that was built to hold the log up so it won't fall. If it falls, it is believed to have bad luck on the side which the log falls toward.

After they put the log up, they have their ceremonial dances, and when that is done with, the Medicine Lodge Woman gets a proper big meal which she missed for four days. And the next day the Sundance breaks up.

The Women's Society and the Horn's Society are important persons. The Women's Society have their ceremony for four days; when they break camp, the Horn's Society start theirs. The Horn's Society used to have four dances in the old days, but now they only have two.

When they used to pray to make rain, or to heal a person who was sick, it all came true: but now only a few of their prayers come true. Their prayers are not as powerful as they used to be since the outlaws came and took over with the churches. They let their way of praying alone, and just prayed the way the outlaws taught them, except at Sundances.

It is true what they say – we won't have any more Sundances in the future, because the old people who know a lot about them are dying off. There are not many old people or people who know much about the Sundances nowadays.

SHIRLEY EAGLESPEAKER,
Alberta

TIME OF PRAYER

We have Sundance about the first week of August: we have it because it is the only time we can all get together to have our prayers.

The Sundance is held about three miles east of Stand-off.

The first one to camp at the Sundance is the Head Chief of our Reserve and the Head of the Horn's Societies. Then all the other people that want to join the Sundance start camping too.

It lasts for ten days, unless anything is holding it up: then we have it for two weeks. Rain, for instance, often holds up the Sundance.

The first to start their business are the Women's Societies. They have their prayers for four days: all this time they have ceremonial dances and prayers in their tents. They don't have their dances outside like the Horn's Societies. The fourth day, they dance early in the morning about six o'clock, and everybody gets up early to join the dance.

Then the Horn's Societies have their prayers and holy dances.

They have two teepees in the centre, and nobody can go into those teepees except the members of the Horn's Societies and the people that are sick and want the Horns to pray for him or her.

They dance a lot different from the Women's Societies: they have the privilege of dancing outside, where it's nice and cool.

The first dance, they dance around the outside of the camps, go to the centre, and sit down on the ground. Then all the people go to the centre and sit around the Horn's Societies in a circle. Then they dance for a little while. After that, they serve lunch to all the people, and after they finish lunch, they dance again. The Head of the Horn's Societies dances first, and then shoots up in the sky: that means the dance has ended.

The second dance is danced only in the centre, not on the outside of the camps. Then they serve lunch again.

The last two days, the Horn's Societies go down to the woods to chop down the biggest tree, and that tree is called 'The Medicine Lodge Pole'. The day before the big dance, they make a place where we can have our last big dance, and put the Medicine Lodge Pole in the centre. That night, all the young people that are interested in the white man's dances have their last big dance; it lasts until about two or three o'clock in the morning.

The last day, all the old people wear their Indian costumes, if they want to, to the dance. In the morning there is a parade. Everybody who wants to join the parade goes down to the woods and gets some branches of leaves, and carries them in the parade around the camp. The big dance comes about two o'clock in the afternoon. All the old people who wore their Indian costumes dance, and it ends about six o'clock that night.

Then everybody breaks up camp, and the Sundance is over until next year.

FAYE WEASEL FATT,
Alberta

AUTUMN RAIN

The rain is falling down
To the ground
And I can smell
The sweet farewell
Of autumn leaves turning brown.

It comes by leaps and bounds
And only sounds
Like some strange bird
That can be heard
For miles and miles around.

SHIRLEY ANNE BUCHANAN,
Nova Scotia

THE DITCH

Everyone was clean. I was clean; my parents were clean; in fact everyone I knew was clean. I lived in a spotless mansion with spotless furniture and slept in an immaculate bed. At night, after I had washed, I would climb into my germless bed in my germless room and take a deep breath of invigorating, germless oxygen. I would then go to sleep, dreaming of what it would be like to have a bit of dirt on the end of my smallest finger.

My goal was attained when my aseptic parents decided to take me for a drive. Oxygen tanks were installed in our car, in fact, in all cars, by the order of 'little sister', who watched over us continually. As we drove over the sterilized road I looked longingly at the dirt in the fields which no one was allowed to touch. Rounding a sharp turn, our smooth tire (made so it wouldn't pick up dirt) slid and I was thrown out of the car. Over and over I rolled in dirt. Dirt was in my hair, dirt covered my entire body and dirt was in my mouth. I instantly broke out in large sores. Never having felt pain before, I was knocked out instantly.

In the hospital, I made a recovery which took five years. How happy I was to be clean again!

Now I am an old man. I am clean, my relatives are clean. In fact everybody I know is clean.

ROBERT MELVILLE,
Ontario

BIG DECISION

There was an excited buzz of conversation as the committee moved forward. Only Melanie was not chattering. She sat quietly leaning forward, her dark eyes shining. She was just as excited as anyone else, but she sat waiting, wondering.

Of course it would be all right; she believed that really, only she had to be sure. The Carnival was such a marvelous thing, and this was the first year their class could be in the parade; freshmen and sophomores weren't eligible. The parade was the big thrill of the year. A sort of Mardi Gras – gay, frivolous, with its decorated floats pretty as cherry blossoms, and the marching units colourful as a circus.

The voice of the chairman hastily brought her back to the present.

"So," Joan Cox was saying, "I want you all to hear Lynne's idea. Go ahead, Lynne."

"Well," began Lynne in an eager rush of words, "I found some perfectly heavenly gauze-stuff at a little wholesale place that sells window decorations. It has a shimmery surface. It costs only a little more than crepe paper and is a hundred times more effective."

She paused and drew out a handful of samples, iridescent wings of cloud, all colours of the rainbow.

"But explain your idea for the costumes for the theme of the float," urged Joan.

She took the chalk and they all watched as a picture grew under her hand, on the blackboard. A lovely wing, with delicate, etched markings took shape.

"Lynne, that's beautiful!"

"Mind you, they'll be quite a trick to make," admitted Lynne. "They have to be stretched on wire."

"And we could wear swim suits for the body part . . ."

Blissfully they passed around the samples, choosing colours, giving advice.

"Both these blues are so pretty, I can't make up my mind."

"This pale yellow for me."

"Oh, yes, Sandy. Perfect!"

Melanie, too, nodded agreement to the other girls, fingered the fragile strips of gauze, and chattered, but she made no claim of her own.

Then someone picked up a piece that was a rich peacock green, a deep jewel colour.

"Melanie, that would be marvelous for you," cried Lynne.

"Don't you have a swim suit almost exactly that shade?"

"I'd love that," she said simply.

Inwardly, she let out her breath in a long sigh of relief. So it was all right. Everyone took it for granted that she was to be with the rest of them. Perhaps it was silly to have doubted it, but she'd had no means of knowing. The question had never come up since she became a student at University High.

And maybe it was silly to remember that other time, away back in grade school. The time when her class was supposed to be a chorus of angels in the school Christmas play—that is all except Melanie, who instead appeared as an attendant to one of the Three Kings of the Orient—the only girl taking a boy's part. Of course, they were tactful about it, pretending it was something special for her, but Melanie knew with a perception sharpened by experience, even at that age, that it was because the teacher thought it might spoil the effect to have a Negro angel in the midst of all those pink and white faces.

But her mind was too busy to dwell on past heartaches. She was picturing the Carnival, with its gay crowds and all of them in their butterfly costumes. Maybe just this once she'd use some of that new make-up, that she had seen in the store only today.

Only she'd have to keep it a secret from her father and just hope that he wouldn't notice it from the spectators' stands. He'd be terribly upset; he'd think she was ashamed and she certainly was not, but father was so proud and serious about things like that. He was editor of the Negro newspaper in Wellington, and the best father in the whole world. They'd always been very close, he and Melanie. That was why she always worked so hard and got good grades—to please him, so that he could be proud of her but he wouldn't understand how it was for a girl. That sometimes you didn't want to stick out like a sore thumb. You just wanted to be part of the fun everybody else was having.

The meeting was just breaking up when Miss Carlson appeared in the doorway.

"Melanie," she called. "Melanie Morris. Mr. Holdsword would like to see you in his office."

The principal's office, thought Melanie wonderingly. She couldn't imagine what it was but Miss Carlson looked cheerful.

The next minute the principal was beaming and congratulating her, and all her pleasure was draining out of the soles of her shoes. The Mayor, Mr. Holdsword explained, had decided to sponsor a float in the parade. It was to have a Brotherhood of Man theme featuring flags and costumes of the main nationalities in Wellington. In the centre, holding up the Union Jack, side by side were to be a Negro and a white student, representing the idea of equality under the flag.

"The two students were chosen on their records," finished Mr. Holdsword. "Leonard Mitchen, a senior at South High, is the white boy, and you, Melanie, have been chosen the Negro student. University High is proud of you!"

Melanie stared at the floor. She hardly knew what to say.

"I-I-I'm sorry," she managed at last, "but I won't be able to make it. I have another engagement on that day. A party."

"Oh, but Melanie, I'm sure anyone who knew the reason would excuse you."

Melanie shook her head. "It's a special family thing."

Mr. Holdsword patted her shoulder. "I'm sure your father of all people will understand that this is important enough to make an exception."

"Don't look so upset, dear," added Miss Carlson kindly. "You ask your father this week-end."

Out on the street at last, with her books under her arm, Melanie trailed one foot reluctantly after the other and wished she could go home via Siberia or the South Pole.

A sudden gleam of hope shot through her mind. Maybe she could still join the others on the classroom float, with luck, because after they had chosen someone else for the Mayor's float, much later she could say the plans had been changed. Obviously, they couldn't snatch it away from her successor. She would be free to join the girls.

"Sorry, I'm late," she called as she rushed into the house, "I had to . . ."

But she didn't finish. Her father was standing in the kitchen doorway.

"I made coffee," he said quietly. "Come in here, Melanie, I want to talk to you."

"What is all this about your not being able to appear on the Mayor's float because of some family party? Miss Carlson phoned about half an hour ago. She said you seemed to think we wouldn't let you go."

Panic flew into her face. "Did you . . . what did you tell her?"

"I didn't tell her anything. Frankly, I didn't understand what it was all about, but I thought it must have been something I'd forgotten. I asked your mother. She didn't know either."

Melanie said nothing. "Well?" asked her father patiently. It had to be done. Might as well get it over. She told him the story, flatly, without emotion or apology. His reaction was exactly as she had expected.

"Melanie, I can't believe it!"

He waited but she said nothing.

"Melanie, listen to me. We've a fine liberal mayor in Wellington. He fights constantly to improve conditions for minorities. He's done a lot for us. We've got to back him up in every way possible.

Melanie stared out the window.

"You're a lucky girl compared with many of our People. You go to a splendid school, and this city may not be perfect, but it's a great deal better than most. That's why you have responsibilities towards those who aren't so fortunate."

"I know all that," said Melanie impatiently. "All right, so I'm so very, very lucky."

Her father looked at her searchingly. She wished he wouldn't look so sad.

"I guess you've forgotten Scolville," he said quietly.

She hadn't forgotten Scolville. Scolville was a place where they had once lived. In Scolville there was no use trying; it would never get you anywhere. Just the same . . .

"I get so tired," she said wearily.

"We all do." He laid his hands over hers gently. "But just the same, you've got to go through with this. You know you have to."

"Oh, look," she cried, exasperated, "I'm sorry I lied, but do you have to make so much out of this one thing? They'd get someone to take my place. The world won't come to an end if I'm not up there on the Mayor's float. Surely, just this once . . ."

"It isn't just this once, Melanie, that we're talking about. You know that."

She knew he was right. It was more than that. If she turned back on this, nothing would ever quite be the same between them, because she wasn't a child now, to make a mistake. She was choosing a way, the pattern of her life.

"And if I don't," she challenged, "will you tell them that I,— that it isn't your fault."

"No," he said slowly, "I won't let you down."

She knew he was trying to make her look at him, but she wouldn't meet his eyes. She ran out of the kitchen and up to her room.

Because now he'd made it even worse. She had put him in a difficult position for a person of his reputation, and he made her recognize the fact and accept the responsibility.

But she resented being put on a spot like this because she didn't think it was fair. Sometimes you had a right to please yourself, and it was mean to make you feel guilty about it.

Her heart hardened. He didn't care at all how she felt. All he'd done was preach the same old stuff she'd heard since she was a baby. She wanted to fight him. She wanted to fight everybody.

Yes, just for once she wanted the satisfaction of setting her chin and defying everyone. Well, wild horses couldn't drag her onto the Mayor's float.

How hateful everything was! She threw herself down on the bed. "How I hate everybody," she wailed. Even the pillow bothered her. It was caught between the mattress and the headboard. She tugged angrily, yanked it out. Then with utmost deliberation she hurled it across the room. There was a slither and a crash as the contents of the top of the bookshelves went down like bowling pins. Destruction was new to her and the mess appalled her.

Well, it could have been worse. Only a few things broken. She picked up the broken glass, put it into the wastepaper basket, rearranged the books, and gathered up the spilled debris. Programs, cards, snapshots, she flipped them over stuffing them into a box. The class pictures—Carol, Lynne, Joan, Dolores.

Dolores, once she'd thought Dolores was going to be her friend, over a year ago. Melanie had invited her for supper; they'd had a nice time. Only the next day she'd heard Dolores saying, "Yes, really nice. Her mother is awfully sweet. Only her father, I don't know, there's something about a coloured man." And Dolores of all people with a father like hers. Why, not once since she was born had Melanie's father talked to her the way Dolores' father did the day they scratched his car. Not even today. Hot tears of remorse sprang into her eyes. All her hard resentment dissolved in an onrun of affection. She rushed downstairs and slid sobbing into his arms. "I'll do it," she said with a sad smile. "I suppose I sounded pretty trivial. I don't know if I can make you understand. It was just that for once in my life I wanted to do something gay and foolish."

By the look of pain in his eyes, she knew he understood.

Rosemary Johnson,
Manitoba

TWO POEMS

If I could kneel but once before the rosewood altar
And pour forth my vilest sins until I reeked of cleanliness
Then all the shadows lurking in the corner of the room
Would vanish as before a holy light.

If I could hear but once an angel's voice
As a whisper through a crowded room,
Then if all the moon-faced Sunday morning banged
Unto infinity, I should not mind.

But I hear only the agony of the voice within
Crying that I must seek alone in the temple strewn night
And find my God in those brief faces
That greet each morning with a eulogy of hate.

Our roots are deep in an old man,
His shirt stained, his face unshaven,
As he endlessly repeats the prayers,
And endlessly believes in them.

Now, in an odourless house,
Deserted for the winter months;
The family nestles amid the dialects
That cluster, sunless, on the southern beaches.

And we, the keepers of the book,
Cannot read a word of it,
Unable to understand its meaning,
Consumed in passions of our own creation.

Well groomed, we stand on broadloomed floors
Inhaling deeply the smell of money,
Well-adjusted children of the new era
Blankly awaiting the next pogrom.

DAVID LEWIS STEIN,
Ontario

RICH UNCLES

There are two classes of rich uncles: those who exist and are a source of hope and consolation to their relatives, and those who do not exist at all. My rich uncle belongs to the latter class. Of this I do not complain, however, for it is my privilege and joy to picture him in my mind as I would have him in reality. Meet my uncle.

Uncle Marquis, a short, plump man with small, piercing, dark eyes and a rotund, reddish nose gives those who know him only casually the impression that he is curious, silly, jocose, and slightly conceited. He is unmarried and insists that any eligible ladies of his acquaintance are interested only in his money. For my part, I cannot see how any lady can overlook the fine qualities requisite of a model husband and so characteristic of my uncle.

His clothes bear the ear marks of good taste and fastidiousness. He is also a very learned man, his topics for conversation varying from Chaucer to the latest in atomic developments. His jocosity is one of his most appealing traits of character. Uncle does not openly show any preference for anyone of my family or relatives. However, I know this to be only a disguise for his real feelings towards me. I have often noticed that he endows me with the longest hand-shake, the beamiest smile, or the most expensive gift. For these, and other reasons, I feel sure I am his favourite among his nieces and nephews and will, no doubt, be duly remembered by him as such.

PEGGY MULLALLY,
Prince Edward Island

VACATIONS UNLIMITED

The boat was dull and patchy
That we sailed on Winnescratchy
And the waves rolled us to and fro.
O, we looked a little sickly
When we got to Garapickly,
That haven 'pon the Winnescratchy slough.

The food was flat and horrid
And the climate wet and torrid,
Out beside the Winnescratchy slough,
And when we all went hiking
The trail was to our liking
Except we kept on falling off those cliffs.

O, horses at the haven
We're bound to have a cave-in
Whenever we were on those mountain trails.
O, that week-end 'pon the lake
Really left us in its wake,
Boats and bridle paths all took their toll.

The boat was dull and patchy
That we sailed on Winnescratchy
And the waves rolled us to and fro.
O, we looked a lot more sickly
When we left old Garapickly,
That haven 'pon the Winnescratchy slough.

DAVID KRYGSVELD,
British Columbia

WINNIPEG

The wheat fields flowing with the colour of the Golden Boy;
The Countess, now dead in her own home;
These are your symbols.
You have pioneer blood to make you strong.
You have dreamer's fancy to make you great.

Hardy and brave!
You overcame the drought, the flood:
Nature.
And you are young.

Proud to be the Gateway to the West:
Entrance to a promised land
Of wealth –
And work.

Proud to be the Melting-pot of Canada:
With Scot and Slav and Scandinavian
And all their brothers
United.

Proud to be the Funnel of the West:
Gathering-place of farm and factory
Where grain
Meets train.

Let other cities look with smugness, look upon their little sister;
Let them grow soft with idleness, while you grow strong;
You had La Verendrye and the noblest Earl of Selkirk:
You had firm foundation, and now grow in the sweat of your youthful toil.

PAUL GRESCOE,
Manitoba

MY GRANDFATHER

Before me lay a still form, familiar, yet unfamiliar. Every grizzled hair was in place – something I had never seen before. I recalled his hearty laughter when, as a four-year-old, I put my arm around his neck, ruffled the few remaining hairs on the back of his head, and asked, "Why don't you get some hair seed at the hardware store?"

The ragged edges of his mustache had been carefully trimmed. It reminded me of the neat privet hedge of which he had been so proud. His maxim where the hedge was concerned had been "Offence is the best defence"; so war was declared on aphids, dogs, cats, children, and – when he thought it necessary – his friends who did not share his enthusiasm for privet hedges.

His tiny emerald stick-pin was not in its accustomed place on his favourite tie. He would have bristled with scorn at the Windsor knot at his throat. When I was quite small, he told me that his stick-pin would turn into a curly green snake which would live under the bathtub if he ever told a lie. Sadly, I wished that it had several months before because I had heard my parents discussing his lies about his shortness of breath and dizzy spells.

The corner of his lower lip turned down, but the pipe which had done this lay at home beside his bed. I wondered what would happen to all his pipes, pieces of pipes, pipe-cleaning and repairing tools, cartons of unusual tobacco containers, and all the other impedimenta he considered necessary for pipe smokers.

A basket of white carnations stood above his head on a background of his clan tartan. He had promised to let me try to play his bagpipes on my sixth birthday. That day he took me down the cellar steps on his shoulder and placed me on the stove where I stood to play his chanter. He leaned against his work bench and, stroking his chin, said, "And so you're six years old and think you're big enough to blow my pipes, do you?" He was quite sure that I wouldn't be able to get a sound from them. He took the pipes from the cupboard and handed them to me. I took them, cleared my throat, and spat over the partition into the coal-bin – a procedure my mother thought thoroughly disgusting, but which he considered a necessary preliminary to playing his pipes. I blew and blew, wondering if the bag would ever fill, but finally it felt solid under my arm. I took a deep breath, blew with all my might, and thumped with my elbow – a half-hearted groan was the result. I tried again. This time it worked. His jaw dropped, and his pipe clattered to the floor as I managed to play three bars of "Bonnie Dundee" before the pipes collapsed with a wheeze. He took the pipes from me, tucked me under his arm, and took my birthday present from the cupboard – a kilt of that same tartan.

I, a small, forlorn figure, stood there, remembering. Those merry blue eyes, now closed, would never twinkle again. There would be no more trips "to see things" – first trains, horses, and zoos, later museums and movies. Different people could tell me the same stories, but not in the same fascinating way. There was no one now who understood a child's trials and tribulations, no one to fix roller skates, no one to patch scraped knees. Facing the first real tragedy of my life, I forgot that there were others who did those things just as often, and just as well. My only thought was that I had lost my best friend, favourite confidant, and beloved grandfather.

ANNE RYRIE,
Ontario

INCIDENT ON THE BUS

Amusement on an overcrowded bus generally makes a person forget the stuffiness of the air and enjoy a laugh.

One snowy afternoon last winter I entered a bus and found a vacant seat behind a lady who could scarcely sit down because, besides having her arms full, she had most of the seat piled up with parcels. Set on her head at a jaunty angle, with a sprig of holly waving to and fro, was a hat.

A man entered the bus and among his bundles was a long-handled toy shovel.

"Move back in the rear," yelled the driver.

The man with the toy shovel moved back with the crowd, and without warning, the shovel handle swung around knocking off the lady's hat.

The hat was promptly flattened under a trample of feet.

"My hat! My new hat! You clumsy man, you've ruined my hat!" shrilled the lady, hysterical with wrath.

"I beg your pardon," stammered the frightened man.

"Beg my pardon indeed," sneered the woman. "Do you mean to tell me you have the nerve to say you're sorry?"

By this time the lady had retrieved her flattened headdress and was patting it as if it were a long lost pet.

"I only bought it last week," she almost sobbed.

"How much did it cost?" questioned the man.

"That's neither here nor there," retorted the woman.

"Indeed it is! I spoiled your hat and I shall pay for damages," declared the man.

"You're so thoughtful," jeered the woman sarcastically. "Since you're so generous, the price is ten dollars and twenty-five cents ($10.25) and thirty-one cents (31c.) sales tax," added the lady, after a minute's thinking.

As the man paid her the ten dollars and twenty-five cents and thirty cents of the sales tax he said, "I haven't any one-cent coins, I haven't any change except a twenty-cent piece."

"I have change. Give it to me," commanded the lady in a dictatorial manner.

He gave it to her, and his eyes nearly popped when she gave him nineteen cents change. He alighted from the bus without further argument.

The bus rolled on her route; the lady rode on toward her stop, and on top of all her bundles was the dilapidated hat.

JOE BARBOUR,
Newfoundland

NATURE'S CALL

I feel as free as a breeze
In the trees
In the fall
When the wild geese call

Winging their southern flight
Through the night
Steady and strong
Making my free heart long

To see the geese in their home
Where the foam
Splashes the rocks
And freedom stalks
Abroad the land.

JOANNE MORTON,
Manitoba

FREE VERSE

So your rhyme
Is a crime;
And your beat
Has n – 4 feet
And doesn't match the line before, either.
Then write in free verse – you can put whatever you want to in it.

You've not got to rhyme
But any time
You want to, it's quite all right.

And your metre
Should make the reader
Cry.
That's modern.

And put, in punctuation!
Marks, wherev,er you wouldn?t expect, them.
And leave them out in all the others that s for effect

And then you can have great long lines that really don't mean very much although actually that doesn't matter.
Or little
Wee shor
T things
That
Mean even less
Because
You
've
Run out of ink part way through.

Just so long as you seem very deep and abstruse.
Backwards line a writing by achieved be easily can which.
Or up words by the mixing.

The rhymelesser
The timelesser.
The worser
The free-verser.

Dennis Lee,
Ontario

PROLOGUE AND EPILOGUE

Darkness;
Darkness, and then light;
Flashing, flaming, fiery crimson light;
Burning, brilliant – bathed in scarlet light;
Flying, flashing, smashing through the blackness of the night;
Rocking, quaking, crashing, in the darkness of the night.
So was the world born.

Light;
Light, and yet more light;
Awesome, blinding, golden – light and yet more light!
Bursting on the senses in a whirl of brilliant light;
Banishing the darkness and the gloomy powers of night;
But then it died, and all there was was night.
So did the world die.

Martin Bartlett,
British Columbia

MAKING A DIME GO A LONG WAY

From the old verandah of my childhood home, I watched my grandchildren scampering in the autumn leaves.

There was Amber with her golden ringlets blazing in the bright October sun; Dawn, the tiny one with big brown eyes that would melt a heart of stone; merry Bliss, with his lovable baby ways; and Christopher, who was older than the others and obviously the leader in the game of tossing leaves.

Christopher was racing toward the Red Maple, with Amber not far ahead, seeking shelter. Little Bliss was tagging after Dawn, his idol.

As I watched them, it made my heart seem young again and childhood memories swept over me — days of joy and laughter.

I was brought back to reality by the quietness that had settled over the lawn. Four little bodies, sprawled and half-hidden in the leaves, were deep in thought.

The wind brought their voices my way and as I listened, I found that Dawn had found a dime in the leaves, but since Christopher had thrown the leaves and Bliss had gathered them for him and Amber was on Dawn's side against the boys — they had decided to settle the matter after their own fashion.

Christopher, always the leader, suggested that they should each tell what he would do with the dime, were it given to him, or, as he put it, "how far they could make it go".

Dawn was given the first chance, since she still held the dime. She told of all the pretty paints she had seen at the store and how she would buy them and they would all paint beautiful, beautiful pictures and give them to Mommy and Daddy and Gramps and Granny.

Amber was next. She thought that the most that anyone could get out of a dime was ten beautiful red candies at the Candy Shop. She added hopefully, that if she got the dime she would give them all some of the candy.

Christopher handed the shiny new dime to Bliss next, but Bliss didn't want it then; he wanted to tell what he would do with it last. Christopher, not wishing to quarrel, took his turn:

"If the dime were mine," he said, "I'd buy real strong string and real tough paper and get the new Dutch boy to make me the best kite in all the world – a kite better than any of the other boys."

His eyes still shining with his plan, he gave the dime to Bliss.

Bliss held the wonderful dime in the palm of his chubby hand, just gazing at it for a moment or two, while the others sat there amid the leaves, watching the little boy. His blue eyes were solemn yet purposeful, as he took out his little sling-shot and placed the dime in the rubber band; a second later the dime was far out of sight, lost in the brilliance of the autumn leaves.

"Dere," said Bliss, with his impetuous baby voice, "I guess I made it go furder dan any of you."

JEAN WHITMAN,
Nova Scotia

WINTER ETCHING

Against the icy winter sky,
Their arms outstretched, the bare trees stand
Crowned with chilly whiteness, robed in storm,
Princes – yet alone in their forgotten land.

WENDY M. GATES,
Ontario

ON NE JOUE PLUS BACH AU CIEL!

Mes amis, vous me croirez si vous voulez : l'autre jour, je me suis trouvé, moi misérable pécheur, à la porte du paradis.

Je frappe, saint Pierre ouvre.

'Bon saint Pierre, . . . je . . . je . . . je . . .'

'Vite, vite ! laisse faire les explications et entre.'

A peine la porte est-elle fermée que . . . que je vois . . . devinez qui . . . Mais oui, le bon gros vieux Bach avec une trompette dans la main, et quelle trompette! Longue, dorée . . . Je veux lui crier: 'Eh, Sébastien !' Mais saint Pierre me met la main sur la bouche et me dit à l'oreille : 'Chut! Il s'apprête à jouer et après cela le Père va parler.'

Autour de Sébastien la foule céleste toute en bleu et blanc s'était rassemblée. Les premières notes éclatèrent; les Séraphins se mirent à sautiller et toute la cour céleste fit de même. Après un allégretto, commença un adagio que Sébastien avait composé, me dit un Saint, 'en l'honneur de saint Wolfgang'. Sur le coup, ce nom ne me surprit pas : les saints portent des noms si baroques ! L'adagio se poursuivait, très grave, très triste (j'ai remarqué que tous pleuraient) lorsque soudain je pensai : 'Wolfgang'. Un ange du nom d'Alcancisias me répondit:

'Mais oui, tu connais Médé?'

'Wolfgang Amédeus Mozart ?'

'Si.'

'Mais comment ? Il a réussi à entrer ?'

'Facilement; même qu'on raconte que le Père, un jour d'ennui, envoya Marie le quérir : du Bach pendant un siècle, on en revient, tu sais !'

'Chut . . . fermez-la ou je vous flanque tous les deux à la porte,' de grommeler saint Pierre en fureur.

Lorsque la sonate fut terminée, j'entendis un roulement de tonnerre et je vis jaillir des milliers d'éclairs. Tous se prosternèrent.

'C'est le Père,' me dit Alcancisias.

Et je vis le Père face à face. Il parla :

'Amédeus, lève-toi, et que tes frères te regardent.'

Je vis alors se lever un jeune homme en dentelles blanches. Mon ange me dit : 'C'est sa fête cette année.' – 'Non !' – 'Mais oui, 1756 à 1956. C'est son deux centième anniversaire.'

Le Père reprit :

'Que dans tout le ciel pendant cette année, on n'entende plus que de la musique d'Amédeus.'

'Ah ! on va s'égayer,' me chuchota Alcancisias.

La foule hurla de joie: 'Ainsi soit-il?' Et le Père disparut.

Ce fut ensuite le tour du Fils de nous adresser la parole:

'Demain, il y aura un concert mozartien auquel tous les musiciens doivent participer.'

Aussitôt les professeurs de violon et de piano se mirent à courir, suivis d'une ribambelle de petits musiciens. Je me proposai donc d'admirer les préparatifs, et je me mis en route pour traverser le ciel. Mais voilà que j'aperçois un tout petit homme en tunique blanche, en train de grouper ses élèves :

'Toi, aujourd'hui, tu seras ténor, toi baryton, et toi, essaie soprano.'

Et ils entonnent *l'Ave Verum.* O délices célestes! Jamais *Ave Verum* ne fut plus consolant. Ils se mirent ensuite à pratiquer *la Messe du Couronnement* :

'Aucun choeur céleste n'est aussi brillant,' me chuchote mon ange.

Je passai donc six heures à les écouter: *le Jubilate* tounait, *le Requiem* faisait gémir les ressuscités. Enfin, monsieur Marcel Laplante (car c'était lui) dit à ses élèves: 'Bon travail, mes agneaux. Dix heures de pratique suffiront.'

Et de toute la nuit, on n'entendit que violons, clavecins, pianos, flûtes, trompettes, et même tambours et trombones. Ah ! pensai-je !

combien est insignifiant notre jazz terrestre comparé au jazz divin de Mozart.

Je continuai mon investigation. Mais tout à coup . . . apparition dans le coin gauche du ciel! pas possible! 'Mais,' dis-je à Alcancisias qui me suivait toujours, 'c'est monsieur Ugay, notre célèbre professeur de violon!'

'Saint César? Tu le connais?' 'Ah! en fait de violoniste, tu sais, ni Heifetz, ni . . . ni . . . Il est imbattable. Tiens, ce sont ses élèves. Ecoute-les.'

Les sonates succédèrent aux sonatines, les quatuors aux quintettes et j'entendis même, ô mystère divin, un "diplet" pour flûte douce, flûte grave, fluteau, flutonne, flutette, flutonnette, etc. . . . Ce fut sur-divin!

Mais un son faux m'arracha à mon extase. C'était une note de piano. Je me retournai et, ce que je vis . . .? Nul autre que Lefebvre, notre pianiste de concert:

'Il me semble que je te connais,' lui dis-je.

'Ah! tu sais, c'est le piano qui fausse!'

'Et qui t'enseigne ici?'

'Toujours monsieur Elie . . . tu le connais: Jean! Il est en train de préparer un duo composé par Mozart. Quel homme! Et quels élèves il a! En ce moment ils répètent des sonates pour piano. D'autres se préparent à jouer des sonates pour violon et piano en collaboration avec les élèves de saint César. Nous devons même jouer les cent premières symphonies de Mozart, ses quatre cents derniers concertos et enfin une vingtaine d'opéras, ça va dépendre du temps qu'il nous restera.'

'Tout ça? Dis donc, pourquoi ne pas venir nous donner un petit concert au Collège. Tu te souviens de ton collège, j'espère?'

'Si je m'en souviens! J'y pense tous les jours, et je le trouve bien monotone. Jamais de musique pour vous égayer!'

'Venez donc alors.'

'Ce n'est pas moi qui mène; il faudrait en parler à saints Marcel, Jean, César, et enfin voir le Père lui-même.'

Nous nous mettons donc en route pour rejoindre saint Marcel, mais à peine avons-nous fait deux pas que le tonnerre se met à gronder et les éclairs à nous assaillir . . . c'est le Père lui-même!

Alors, mes amis, vous comprenez bien que j'ai eu peur; je me sentis fondre, dégringoler et voici que je viens d'atterrir. Elle est bien triste cette terre. Ah! oui, une terre sans musique ce n'est pas gai. Mais peut-être qu'ils viendront, les musiciens célestes. Pourquoi pas ?

SERGE ROUSSEAU,
Québec

DAWNING

In the East a glow is making
  Silhouetted clouds creep by.
Colours of the world before us
  In the ever brightening sky.

Lazy clouds cast off their dull grey
  Showing white with golden threads.
Birds, the early morning risers,
  Flap their wings and shake their heads.

Noiselessly the sun comes creeping
  Sending brilliant rays of light
Shooting o'er the star-dazed heavens
  Chasing remnants of the night.

GORDON HAROLD RIDEOUT,
Nova Scotia

RESCUED

Creeping, surging, slipping as quickly as a juggler's hands, the water of the Humber edged toward our home. We, the Griff family, sat on the roof of our house, tense with fear, while we watched the muddy river cover our car and advance another foot. Hour after hour, we waited and stood ankle deep in water, our fingers numb, our bodies stiff with cold. Realizing how dim our chance of escape was, we suddenly heard it – the far-off beat of a motor boat. Heaven knows what it was doing on our part of the river, in its present state. When it came into sight between lifting waves, we could see it was a dory handled by a huddled figure who didn't seem to know the meaning of fear. He attempted to reach us twice, and twice he vainly risked his life in the dangerous circling waters. On the third try he succeeded in reaching us. My mother was taken to safety first, then the rest of us individually, until we were all secure from the reaching waters. The Humber, when compared with other rivers, is said to be calm as a lamb, but we, with hundreds of others, have witnessed it as a lion.

LOVIE TAMO,
Ontario

TOUCHING

They walked up the lane together,
The sky was covered with stars;
They reached the gate in silence,
He lifted for her the bars.

She neither smiled nor thanked him,
Because she knew not how,
For he was just a farmer
And she a Jersey Cow.

PAUL GROSKORTH,
Ontario

CIVILIZATION

The track shivers — the air is nervous as the heat-parched
desert slowly cracks.
Vibrations altered and rhythm begins. A wave pauses —
and moves on.
Behind the yellow skyline — near now — a wisp of smoke
drifts lazily,
And
suddenly
the dot appears.
Buzzing as of a thousand bees, the track hums softly to
itself
In the hot sun; a pickup truck slides up and stops
With a screech of tired brakes, but its sound is soon lost
In the vast naked wilderness of desert, bounded faintly
by a purple line.

The TRAIN appears!
Pushing its massive drivers down as if to beat
The cow'ring rails into submission. Streamlined fury
Devours steel and wood, challenging distance to a duel
Of Giants, as sighing air brakes relax to belch
Their load of steam.
A flying bag, and a hand, a long green panorama
And the Train is gone.
The humming slowly dies.
And desert reigns
Alone.

JOHN A. G. GRANT,
Ontario

ELEGY

The gnarled trees raise their gaunt and twisted
arms, their branches bare,
The last lone leaf flutters down to earth;
The cold dull earth,
The barren earth,
The dead earth.

This is the funeral of mankind,
The moaning wind the only mourner;
This is the burial of his hopes,
The wind's sigh the only prayer;
This, the entombment of his desires,
The wind's roar the only music;
This, the fulfilment of his fate,
And the gaunt trees the only witness.

So let him lie –
This be the requiem of man's desires,
This be the dirge of his achievements,
The circle is complete:
Fate is resolved;
The god created
And the man destroyed:

The ash is ash become,
And the dust, dust.

MARTIN BARTLETT,
British Columbia

NEWFOUNDLAND SPRING

The Highland mists
That come and go
May seem like Elfland
For a day or so
When you are in the Highlands.

But when you live
By the ocean's shore
Where they stay for a month
And sometimes more
They hold no strange beauty.

They are wet and cold,
And the trees are bare,
The flowers sleep,
And the lines of care
Grow deeper on the farmer's face.

"God's weather," you say
"But not His best."
This sickening fog
That rose from the crest
Of the rolling waves in the sea.

HELENA FRECKER,
Newfoundland

HOW TO WIN MARKS AND INFLUENCE MASTERS

The struggle for survival between the master and his flock has dragged on and on through many centuries. This guide should help the pupil to win the battle.

At first glance it may seem impossible to outwit a master. Actually it is fairly simple. Each of their minds is a one-track train trundling over an endless line of Latin, the fall of the Roman Empire, Christopher Columbus, and so on. It is inconceivable to a master that he could be derailed by a mere pupil. Little does he realize how his mind has been worn down by his endless journey.

Masters may be divided roughly (but not too roughly) into three groups, normal, abnormal and those whose minds have skipped their tracks.

A 'normal' master is quiet and sensible. He has taught for many years, and usually has a wife and children. It is very important to note this man's likes and dislikes. For instance, if a master is enthusiastic about football, it is very easy to lead him astray during a boring English period. The same may be done with his extreme dislikes. If one is tired of concentration on the more important aspects of a subject, it is pleasant to lead the master into elaboration on small and unimportant details by pretending an enthusiastic interest. A very important rule with the normal teacher is to laugh convincingly at his jokes, no matter how feeble they may be (and they usually are). This deceives him into thinking he is witty and a pleasant glow will steal into his mind. Another device is to look deeply interested, so that he will feel he is teaching you something. If he asks you a question, however, it is best to admit frankly that you don't know the answer.

It may appear that this normal master is very easy to deceive. But! A word to the wise! Do not push him too far. He is not so gullible as he may appear. It would be a misfortune to push him into the second group with which we are now about to deal.

The typical example of this group is the master who cannot keep order. He shouts, screams, has fits of hysteria. He throws pencils, pens, chalk, ink, desks and sometimes himself at his pupils. In short, his periods are like an afternoon at the Barnum and Bailey circus. Of course these are just occasional fits. He doesn't have them oftener than about five a week. The rest of the time he chews pencils and his fingernails, while wading through a dull period in the midst of a storm of paper pellets, shouting, flying ink, and blind cords which usually wrap themselves around his neck and try to strangle him. It is best to push him at once into the abysmal depths of the third group, and then he may be removed quietly.

I hope this essay will be useful to everyone and will become a standard manual of attack and defence.

This topic was prescribed for a humorous essay. The characters are entirely the product of the author's imagination and have no relation to any masters living or dead or half-dead.

Duncan McLaren,
Ontario

THE FISHPOND

Spots of gold, silver, flashing round,
Darting in and out of weeds, castles, rocks.
The glide, the pause without a sound,
Done both singly and in flocks
By goldfish, minnows in the pond,
Held together by one strong bond—
Captivity.

Wendy Weyman,
Ontario

THE FROG

Crak-ak!
Where is he?
I hear him singing over there — or is he over *there*?
Crak-ak!
If I tip-toe softly towards his voice, I may see him.

So I walk gently over the damp grass,
Following his
Crak-ak!

Is he by the fence?
— Or is it just a root.
Crak-ak!
Is he there in the long grass?
No.
That is just a stone.

Where is he?
He is too well hidden for me to see with my untrained
eye.
Oh well,
I have other things to do.

And as I walk away,
He laughs.
Crak-ak!

JOYCE PULLEN,
British Columbia

WINTER FANTASY

It was sunset in the garden
But not like summer days
For winter's snow a mantle
Arranged in many ways.

Each shrub and tree was covered
With glistening jewels of white
Adorning all the branches
Oh, what a wondrous sight!

The garden chair was all transformed
Into a fairy throne
And silver white were all the twigs
From whence the birds had flown.

Where once had been the garden,
Hidden now from sight,
Were scallops formed of pink ice-cream
Moulded by the light.

The glittering, frosted tree trunks,
Where the wind had blown the sleet,
Stood in ordered row on row
Down the quiet street.

And heavy laden branches,
By weight of snow bent low
Were tinted by the sunset,
And formed a crimson glow.

LLOYD BURRITT,
British Columbia

THE END OF THE STORY

Edmond Turner, the famous author, was drunk. He was extremely happy, and he had a very good reason to be so. He was celebrating the completion of the book that he had been writing for the last half-year—at least he had finished it in his mind. The rest of the book had been written several months earlier, but the last few chapters of the story had been difficult to complete.

It concerned a mystifying crime which had baffled the best criminologists in the world. Someone had been killed with a knife, but all the doors were locked and all the windows bolted from the inside. No one could have been able to enter the room. Moreover the dead man had not committed suicide, because the knife was in his back.

Mr. Turner had written the story without knowing the solution to the mystery. However, under pressure from his publishers he had submitted the first twenty chapters hoping to work out a satisfactory ending as he went along. This hadn't been easy; in fact he had been losing his health, his reason, and had almost defaulted his contract before he came across the startling answer. It was ridiculously obvious, yet only a genius would have been able to imagine it.

And now he was seated at a small table in an Inn drinking whisky. He was very excited and happy, and he wanted to tell someone the fascinating ending of his story. Then he noticed a short, meek looking man, with grey hair and glasses who was passing beside his table. Mr. Turner introduced himself and persuaded the man to sit with him.

Soon they were good friends and Edmond began to tell his story.

By the time he had finished recounting the story and had said goodbye to his agitated companion, the Inn was closing. Mr. Turner left the Inn reeling slightly, and started on his way home. His head ached and everything seemed foggy in front of his eyes. He lost his balance and fell down heavily banging his head on the sidewalk. Struggling to his feet, he gingerly touched the gash on his forehead, and shaking his head as if to clear away the cobwebs, stumbled home.

The next morning Edmond sat down to his typewriter and began to type out the end of the story, but he could not remember the solution. He tried for two hours to recall it, but he could not. In desperation he remembered that he had been at the Inn yesterday, that he had told the solution to a man . . . his name? . . . he did not know it . . . Phone him perhaps? . . . But he did not know the man's phone number nor his address. What could he do? Without the ending, the story was worthless.

Then an idea struck him. He phoned the newspapers and put in an advertisement. Now, if the man who was at the Inn last night reads the paper, he will come and tell him the solution.

The next day he examined the paper and found his advertisement. But to his horror and astonishment, he found the following story beside his announcement. A woman had been found in her room with a knife in her back. The police who were summoned by the woman's husband, disclosed an incredible fact. The doors and windows of the room had been locked from the inside, and it was impossible for anyone to have entered.

Edmond Turner was frightened. The husband of the woman must have been the man to whom he had told the story. Now it was absolutely necessary for him to remember the solution, and quickly! He locked the doors and windows and sat down at his desk. He thought. Suddenly he remembered. But it was too late, for as the idea came back to him a hot breath brushed his neck and a cold blade penetrated deep into his back. Edmond Turner's story was finished — forever!

JACKIE M. ABELLA,
Ontario

THE NORTHERN LIGHTS

Across the darkened sky they flash in splendour
Dancing, flitting, then eerily dashing away
Reds and greens and blues all ever changing
The aurora borealis, like a jewelled spray.

Quickly do they come and quick do they depart
Weirdly lighting up the heavens as they flee
These ever changing ribbons of glory and of awe
Like moonlight on a stormy billowing sea.

Their mysteries are unknown and their tales have not
been heard,
Of the bleak and frozen land from whence they rise,
The glorious Northern Lights of the barren Arctic lands,
The midnight rainbow of the Northern skies.

DALE FRY,
Yukon

WENDIGO

There's a night in an Indian legend
Where the Wendigo walks again:
A chieftain killed once in a battle
Who brings his revenge to men.

The conditions are right for the Wendigo
When thunder racks the sky;
Mothers clasp loved ones to heaving breasts
And pray he'll pass them by.

The brave and dauntless warrior
  Hides a tear that blinds his eye
For the lightning is bright, and the thunder right
  And perhaps his baby will die.

Oh, what grief so poignant!
  A heavy cross to bear
When the baby starts to whimper
  And they sense that 'he' is there.

Every louder clap of thunder
  Is answered with a sigh
For the Wendigo is seeking
  For a baby who will die.

Oh, such agony of feeling
  In the heart he fills with dread!
Each moment is so precious
  Just one kiss before he's dead!

A vigil of pain, a night of grief
  For they know that a baby must die;
Evil walks with the Wendigo
  When thunder racks the sky.

VALERIE FINDLAY,
Ontario

FREE FALL

George Harmer adjusted the range on his latest invention. He did not yet know what its possibilities were, but its effect could be unusual. From his hotel room in the Royal York he could see a portion of the Scarborough Bluffs. He turned the power a little higher and picked up his field glasses. A stone at the bottom shook a little and then dislodged itself from the clay. It stayed about eight inches above the ground until the wind blew it out of the ray. He turned to scan the countryside. There was a girl approaching the field of distortion. He settled back to watch.

It was a beautiful day and the air had that sharpness that it has only in September. Ellen was walking along admiring the beautiful landscape. The wind rustled the trees and sent the leaves swirling around.

She was fascinated by the antics of the wind and became almost hypnotized. She wanted to start running and skipping after the leaves and go floating along with them. Her feet seemed much lighter and seemed to move of their own volition. The cliff in front of her brought her to her senses, and she stood and watched the leaves go gently floating down at the whim of the wind. She had a strange desire to follow them down, and felt that she could go floating down just as lightly and easily as the leaves. This feeling was so strong that she just stepped off into space.

She was immediately swept up by the wind, and instead of falling, she went gently falling down. She was not surprised; she knew it would happen.

Her mind was very relaxed and she didn't actually realize what was happening. Suddenly, before she realized it, she had landed and was standing at the bottom of the cliff. Ellen's mind was in a whirl, and she was terribly confused. She had enjoyed the sensation, but did not know whether she had dreamed it or whether it really had happened. She wanted to do it again and again; it seemed so relaxing, so easy, and so wonderful. Her feet seemed as light as a feather and she still seemed to be floating. After all the tension in Ellen's office and that fight with Harry, this was the answer to all her problems. She tried going floating down again. It was the same thing all over again. She spent all afternoon floating down the hill. When she went home that night she felt like a different woman.

Harry was strangely cold and quiet all through supper. When they were sitting together in the living room reading, she tried to bring up the strange adventure she had had that afternoon.

He reacted very strangely. First, he seemed startled, but after a few minutes he nodded his head understandingly.

"You'd better go to bed dear; you've been working too hard," Harry said soothingly. But she knew he didn't mean it.

She tried to explain, to convince him that it really happened. He had that air of false understanding that is so frustrating.

Oh yes, he understood. Sure, he believed her.

"Now you just go to bed early, get a good night's sleep, and it will be all gone in the morning."

That last one was all that Ellen could 'take'. She tried to convince him. She pleaded, she cajoled, and stamped her foot, but it only seemed to make Harry's soothing even more false and unpleasant.

In the morning Harry had some news. "We're going to the city, Ellen. You're going to see a doctor who can help you."

Ellen was not surprised. Harry was like that, so stubborn and so positive that he was right that she had no other choice but to go.

The psychiatrist's office was well furnished and very comfortable. The nurse, or secretary, or whatever she was, was quiet. She asked the questions in a way that suggested it was just a routine case. The psychiatrist himself was sympathetic but persistent. He asked many questions, and from time to time jotted things down. He left her alone in the office and went to talk with Harry. He came back a little later, beaming.

"Well, your illness isn't too serious," he said pleasantly. "You'd better take a few weeks holiday. Don't do anything; just take it easy and relax. Come back in three weeks and we'll see how you feel."

That was Monday. On Tuesday she went out again to the field where it all began. The wind was very strong that day and she had trouble keeping herself under control. She didn't float now, but went rushing from one place to another. On the top of the cliff she looked down and saw someone standing there. She floated down to him as quickly as she could. He was a hunter, dressed as such, but the man belied his dress.

Ellen tried to talk to him. She asked him what he had seen. Had he really seen her float down from the cliff top? Did he believe what he saw? Did he think she was mad? He just looked at her. She smelled the liquor on his breath. The man slowly turned and walked unsteadily away, muttering, his hip pocket bulging with a bottle. She would have to find a more reliable witness to convince Harry.

Apparently the doctor had instructed Harry to humour her. When Ellen asked him on Wednesday to accompany her on her walk, he immediately consented. The day was beautiful, the sun shone brightly and everything seemed perfect. Ellen had a curious sense of foreboding but she tried to shrug it off. She waited until Harry was watching her then she stepped off.

The C.B.C. was having trouble. Someone was working with some sort of device that interfered with their broadcasting. All Wednesday morning their inspectors had been working to pinpoint the disturbance. They found it was a room on the east side of the seventeenth floor of the Royal York. They sent their inspectors with their tracing equipment to that particular floor.

George had a twinge of pride when he noticed that the girl had someone with her. Here was someone who could verify the effects of his invention. He checked to make sure all was well in the wiring of his invention. He saw the girl take one step out into space. Suddenly there was a knock on the door. He heard an authoritive voice "Inspectors. . . ."

Quickly he shut off his machine and pushed it back under the bed. He got up to open the door. . . .

As soon as she had taken that first step she knew something was wrong. She couldn't float, the magic had gone. She screamed as the earth rushed up to meet her. . . .

DAVID PERRY,
Ontario

NIGHT

Night is a cat
Springing up silently —
Swiftly — a gray cat,
A black cat,
Out of the west.

Night is a flood of darkness
Of softness
Inundating the land
Drowning the noisy, traffic-filled street
In cool, liquid velvet.

Night is a fog
Rolling silently through the gaudy streets,
Pierced and torn by the harsh, unfeeling lights
Of the callous city.

Night is a woman,
Caressing the concrete canyons
With soothing fingers —
Bringing respite to a world
Ravaged by the cruel day.

PAUL R. VAN LOAN,
Ontario

LACE

What lace is so rare—
What lace can compare—
With the lace of a perfect snow-flake?

Or the lace cast by shadows of lilacs?

Or the lace of a rainbowey cobweb . . .
Tinted by sunbeams?

Or the lace-work of age
On a tired old face?

God made no finer lace!

MAY MOON

The dewy cool
Of the evening air
Hangs misty and blue over the fading
Sunset . . .
The faraway shore,
Fringed with green,
Is a carpet for the early
May Moon . . .
She rises—
A great, pale, luminous
Sphere. Pink on the rim
Of the night,
She lingers
For only a moment—for
A last look at day;
Then floats
Up the path of the sky
To her realm of stars.

MERLE SAWATSKY, Saskatchewan

AN ODOROUS EXPERIENCE

Coming home from a friend's house, one night a few winters ago, I had a most hair-raising experience. As it was late and I had to be home at a certain time, I tried to take the shortest way possible.

The shortest way was through an old field that much resembled a deserted graveyard with its moss-covered black and white stones of all shapes and sizes.

Boldly I started off. Climbing over an old rickety fence, I became enveloped in the tall grass. Upon much search I finally found the beaten track.

"Oooo-ooo-ooo!" The wind was rustling through the grass. Over in the corner of the lot a tall maple was doing a mad dance as its wrinkled leaves were blown to and fro. Up in the sky no stars glimmered, just the man in the moon had chosen to show his face.

I looked back to see that no one was following me. In that moment, Mother Skunk hustled her brood across the path. All of the babies crossed. All, that is—except one.

On I hurried, thinking of all the nightmares I'd ever had. Step by step I drew nearer to the black and white ball of fur. Suddenly, I felt something soft underfoot. In such an eerie background, I thought for sure it was something horrible. Quickly, I dashed away. Alas! I was too late. I did not get away in time to escape that beautiful scent that most skunks carry. This one was no exception. By the time I reached home the perfume had soaked through the pedal-pushers I was wearing.

The next morning saw me digging a hole, and, later, burying a bundle of clothes. After the funeral I made up my mind to take no more shortcuts, even if I had just one minute to get home in.

Charlotte G. Haldenby,
Yukon

THE PET GIRAFFE

Of all the animals at the zoo,
I like the best of all
The handsome, voiceless giraffe,
Who is so very tall.

When I grow up I'll keep a giraffe,
And have him as a pet.
I also hope to ride him
Although I don't know how to yet.

I wonder what I'll call him;
Spotty a good name would be.
I wonder what he'll look like;
I'll have to wait and see.

JACQUELINE TASCHEREAU,
Nova Scotia

ENGLISH FORTY

To write good poetry you have to be an inspired genius. If you're inspired, and like me, you come up with a jumble of words of which maybe one line is good poetry. If you are a genius and not inspired you come up with a great bunch of words that mean something only to the poet's mother; unfortunately she died years earlier. And then there are the people like me who either get inspired or get expired from their English class. This results in the worst poetry of all.

I started a sonnet once on my own; a few weeks later it became an English assignment. I had the first stanza and ideas for a punch line done on my own:

Do you not find it hard to understand
How He gave air and water on the sand,
Gave light and darkness for the land. And then,
As if it's not enough, created men!

And, for the punch line:

The Bible explains it, scientists too;
They're different versions; which one's true?

I tackled the rest as I would any English 40 assignment – not hell nor high water would make it come to me.

Last summer Seton Lake, a very beautiful lake, inspired me at dusk.

Silently night, from a Seton Sight,
  Creeps in;
And the shadows fall, round one and all,
  From the mountains.

One of the boys called me over and that's as far as I ever got – not that I should go any farther.

One Sunday, a very beautifully lazy day, I wrote – at least attempted – another poem. As before I didn't give 'two hoots' whether it was all iambic tetrameter or trochaic hexameter; I just wrote!

GEORGE SLINN,
British Columbia

THE DAY REGINA BLEW DOWN

The day was hot and humid,
One hundred and five in the shade,
The peaceful calm in the Sunday air,
Was just a masquerade.

Two hours after mid-day,
Tension began to rise,
And toward the south a column of gray,
Rose up toward the skies.

The sky grew dark and heavy,
The air grew still as night,
This was the scene in Regina,
Ere the storm vent its might.

The wind screamed through the city,
The heavens unleashed their wrath,
Straight as an arrow it whined and whirled,
And ruin marked its path.

Foundations cracked and crumbled,
The lake was churned to foam,
Debris went flying through the air,
And children ran for home.

A few short minutes later,
The cyclone's course was run
It left a wrecked and shattered town,
Its fearful work was done.

The cyclone now is over,
And many years have flown,
But always we'll remember,
When Regina blew down.

Marian McGirr,
Saskatchewan

NIGHT WIND

Wind, wild wind,
Whistling through the tree tops,
Whistling through the pine trees,
Incessant and fierce.
Loud, angry, rushing sound
Filling the tree tops,
Bending their boughs down
Low to the ground.

Waves, wild waves,
Breaking on the beaches,
Breaking o'er the rocks,
Incessant and fierce.
Loud, angry, roaring sound
Filling the cold air,
Whipping the lake to
White-caps around.

Dark clouds sailing
All across the skyways,
Before the driving wind,
Incessant and fierce.
Covering the Milky Way,
Covering the moon up,
So nothing but wind
And darkness abound.

ANNE C. BEGOR,
Quebec

ECLAIRS

Sommeil de ma chambre quand je veille
Une lampe assoupie
Conseils des vents dans la fenêtre
Moi je ne dors pas.

Maisons ténébreuses et noires
Portes verrouillées et cadenas rouillés
Pianos endormis et sonates muettes
Pipes éteintes et cigarettes inachevées
Moi je ne dors pas.

Robes de chambre sur les chaises
Porte-manteaux gonflés
Vêtements jetés çà et là pour le sommeil
Souliers délacés et vidés de leurs pieds
Chemises déchirées. A rapiécer.
Chapeaux transpirés et bérêts accrochés
Moi je ne dors pas.

Paniers remplis de feuilles blanches
Poèmes commencés
Lunettes cassées sur le ciment et laissées là
Journaux pliés et déjà vieux d'une journée
Discours publiés et oubliés
Chansons de minuit qui ne chantent plus
Encre séchée
Moi je ne dors pas.

Lampadaires cachés dans les branches des arbres
Clôtures enfoncées et défoncées
Automobiles arrêtées et refroidies
Eglises et religions barrées et enfermées
Tavernes sans boisson de nuit

Sérail abandonné
Bibliothèque à plâtre gris
Réveille-matin réglés pour sept heures
Moi je ne dors pas.
Tous.

Nuit aux éclairs trouvés avec rage
Peur de ne pas tout voir
Illuminations remplaçant le sommeil
Météores qui traversent le ciel en sifflant
Pour toi nuit
Mai je ne dors pas.

Pas de salamalecs
Plus de fard
Seulement la nuit pleine de lumière
La nuit aux colosses mystiques
La nuit à l'étoile solitaire
La nuit solitaire qui a pensé et qui pense
Quelques-uns.

Quintessence
Brillante lactescence
Nuit éblouissante
Je ne peux pas dormir
Je ne veux plus dormir.

Jean Garon,
Québec

A DAY OF HOOKEY

The two urchins deviously skirted the little school and entered the woods by a sunless path. It was a typical, sunny, summer day, the perfect day to play hookey with the intriguing prospect of a lazy leisure of fishing. Jocundly, the mischievous truants trod their way down the shady aisles of the woods and emerged into a keyhole-like clearing through which a wide, rushing stream ran.

With some thick, cumbrous ropes that they had 'crooked' along the way, and a few stray, drift logs they constructed a crude raft which was uncomplimentary to any form of the art of carpentry. Beckoned by the challenging voice of adventure, they shoved off, intrepid of their plight, and were quickly swept into mid-stream by the flowing current.

The farther downstream they went the calmer the stream became, and finally it broadened into a still pool which was their private fishing hole fringed with sundry trees and tall grass. Probing among the grass, they came up with two fishing poles and a can of worms which they had purposely furnished the day before when the inspiration of their daring escapade of truancy first dawned upon them.

"Say, Bill, who's that over there?" asked Mickey, pointing a curious finger at an unknown personage who apparently had invaded their clandestine hide-out.

"Search me. It's the first time I've seen him here. He looks like a tramp t' me," Bill replied after scrutinizing the stranger some time.

And indeed his mien alluded to such a true revelation. The soles of his shoes were bidding adieu to the rest of the footwear, and the friendship had probably been a long and enduring one. His pants by their style and squalid visage had seen action in the Spanish-American War, while his jerkin which once had boasted of a sheepskin covering had been sheared by perpetual wear, and was splitting at the seams in places. A month's growth of beard covered his weather-beaten countenance and appended to the unparalleled magnetism that enticed them to approach the stranger. He was sitting on a tiny, grassy declivity by the stream, chewing a straw and looking carelessly at the water.

"Hi!" said sanguine Mickey, throwing a fervent salutation in the direction of the tramp.

Startled, the latter looked up and about him as if called from a profound sleep by an unknown voice. At first he glanced uncertainly about, not knowing whence the interjection came but he sighted the boys and said as if his perplexity had vanished: "Hello, there."

They slumped heavily to the ground, baited their hooks, and cast their lines in the stream. All the while the stranger watched, a strange affection shining in his brown eyes.

"Say, boys," said the tramp whom the boys surmised to be around sixty-three.

"Yes?"

"Well," he said, running his fingers through his near grey hair, "I was wonderin' . . . would youse mind givin' me one of your fish if youse catch any; I ain't et for near two days."

"Sure, you can have all we catch," Mickey offered. "We never eat them anyway, do we Bill?"

"Nope," acquiesced Bill.

"Thanks a heap, boys. It's not very often that I have the fortune to run into charitable souls."

"How is that?" queried Mickey, genuinely steeped in the fascinating creature.

"Well," explained the tramp as a facetious grin traversed his thin lips, "you just might say that I'm an outcast of society, spurned by all classes. A sorta black sheep — the rotten apple of the barrel or the dog that nobody wants. But as long as I have the open road afore me I'm happy, yes, sir."

"Guess you've seen everything and been everywhere," implied Bill filled with urging interest that might satisfy his longing for awful, blood-tingling tales.

A reminiscent light shone in the tramp's eyes for a moment and then he said vauntingly: "Boys, I've bin as far north as Alaska, as far south as Mexico, as far west as the Pacific, and as far east as the Atlantic. I've bin through thick 'n thin, seen fights, murders, bloodshed, thievin', and a dozen other crimes. I've bin in jail, but only for vagrancy; all my life I've travelled the road and I'll die on the road, I warrant."

There was a sudden tug at Bill's line and his reward was a good-sized pickerel. While the inquisitive boys put the nomad to more interrogations, the latter began making preparations for the frying of the delicious-looking morsel.

"Are you staying around here much longer?" Mickey asked.

"Not me, son. I'm headed for California. I ain't never bin there and I think it's about time I had. This here place is just another stop-over for me. I'm takin' the first train out tomorrow."

Bill fixed his legs Indian style and said: "Guess it's pretty exciting!"

"What's pretty exciting, son?" asked the tramp, turning the fish over on the kindled fire with great dexterity.

"Why travelling the way you do," answered Bill, "on the trains, I mean."

"Well, I don't know if you'd call it exciting," the tramp replied with a smile. "I'm cold in the winter and for days all year round I go without a crumb of food. I'm fortunate if I have one square meal a day. The railroad dicks are forever on my heels like hounds and I have to high-tail it like an animal a-running for its life."

At this point in his autobiography the tramp clamped his teeth like a vice on the fried fish, ran his teeth along it as if it were a corn on the cob, smacked his lips, sighed, wiped his mouth on the back of his sleeve, and fell contentedly back on the grassy slope.

The fascinated lads had observed his gormandizing manner of eating which was not unlike that of savages whom they had read about in books, but the picturesque creature was such a singular novelty, seldom if ever seen in the vicinity, that they condoned his failings of etiquette. Inwardly they envied the vagabond for he was not shackled to any form of responsibility but had the coveted liberty that every soul pines for, and the knowledge that one gets only from travel.

"Say, how did you ever become a . . . traveller?" inquired Mickey.

"Well, son," began the pariah, reflecting for a moment, "it started—that is the itch for roamin'—I figger, when I was just a kid aroun' your age, I reckon. Nobody could keep me in school."

He put rebellious emphasis on the word 'school' with a sort of blissful triumph, and continued:

"I hated the school, the conceited teacher who was forever boastin' of his possessions and experiences, and the borin' quiet of the room. It all went agin the grain of my likin'. So I'd skip every chance that came my way. There was a great woods close by our school with a river just teemin' with fish; I'd fish there and go swimmin' and hikin' in the woods. They kept bringin' me back, and I'd keep runnin' away until I ran away permanently. Yep, I guess playin' hookey was what made me what I am now. Probably the cause of a lot of other fellers in the same situation, too."

Rolling over on his side, the tramp said with levity, "I guess you boys like school, though."

"Yea, I suppose its okay," Bill replied unenthusiastically, "except for Miss Harrow, our teacher; she's about as attractive as an undertaker."

The tramp laughed, and gave an apprehensive nod. Then he inquired:

"Say, shouldn't youse be at school now?"

Bill stole a glance at Mickey, and Mickey looked uneasily at Bill. Mickey racked his brain for a reliable lie. He said:

"Oh, we got a holiday, today, on account of our class is having a picnic."

Deeming this somehow unsubstantial, the tramp asked:

"Then why aren't youse at the picnic?"

This query arrested them on their stumbling path of falsehood. Mickey answered, reeling in his line,

"We're leaving for it right now."

The gaudy vagabond was blandly smiling as the two truants treaded the log that arched over the stream and headed into the woods. The sad reprimanding that they received at the school was incidental, for they possessed no flourishing cupidity to be future tramps to which inevitably their paths were leading.

DAVID BENSON FRENCH,
Ontario

GREY MORNING

A long hour in a cold room;
A tired teacher talking;
A sharp bang; a slow boom;
A lone workman walking!

Grey gull on a wide hook;
Grey sky swift-clouding;
Eyes slip from the dreary book
And the grey thoughts come crowding.

ANDRÉE INGRAM,
British Columbia

ELM

The sudden staccato of rustling leaves,
Wind-borne and wild in smoky dust:
An elm stands lonely among harvest sheaves
Carpeting fields with golden rust.

As sunlight dies, its blackened form lies stark,
Leafless, as now it will remain
Until the day the lilting meadow-lark
Flies through the furrowed fields again.

Paul Grescoe,
Manitoba

BLACK HOURS

O hallowed darkness
Passing by
Connecting day
To day.
In evening
Anticipated,
In morning
Reminisced.

Divine, the peace,
Rest abounds
Dream, think,
Ponder long
In solitude of
Night, no loneliness
But tranquility
And placidness.

This glory broken
By faint glitters
Stars and moon
The milky way,
Car lights, streets,
House lights, stores,
Others made
Of human cause.

Noiseless, save
The wing flit
Or the call, both
Bird and beast,
Wind whistle,
Tree tremble,
Silent breaking
Of the night.

Dawn – the victor
Bringing creatures
Running, driving,
Banging, tearing,
Now we looking
Into hours when
The crazed rush
Stops again.

DONALD ARTHUR WYLIE,
Ontario

GOD'S COUNTRY

I see now the golden sun-tanned mornings,
Where high above, a majestic ball of fire
Guards God's country.

I see the fresh and twinkling evenings,
Where high above the black space, the ever-watchful
Luna
Peers across the bleak and misty caverns,
And watches over God's country.

I see the rushing water of the silver cataracts,
Plunging down upon the rocks below,
and bursting forth their joy,
For they are in God's country.

But half the world yawns between me
and this land . . .
And all I do is dream.

Nicholas Rallis,
Ontario

PRESENT DAY PIONEERS

One year ago when I looked out the train window at the small settlement which was to be my new home, I felt as though I was at the end of everything. To me, having come from the busiest section of the modern city of Vancouver, this looked like the dreariest part of a wilderness. I found myself comparing the unadorned, hard working women with the smartly dressed Vancouver people I was used to seeing. As I looked over the small railway station with the cluster of houses around it, I could not help remembering the tall apartment buildings, paved streets, and the blocks of up-to-date dress shops in the city. Indeed, I could not think why Dad had picked this lonely outpost for a new home!

That was my first impression of Greenwood, a small logging settlement in Northern British Columbia, where my father had brought us to live, because, in his own words, he was "sick and tired of wearing his feet out on cement sidewalks". As the days passed, I learned more about Greenwood. I found that everything was simple and everyone was unaffected. There were no washing machines, refrigerators, or electric stoves because there was not any electricity. There was no theatre, just a hall which was used for everything from a square dance to a Christmas concert. The railway station was the centre of excitement, especially when the train came three times a week, carrying the mail and supplies. In the station waiting room behind a counter, these things were stacked and that was the community store.

At first I was dismayed at the simplicity of the house in which we were to live, but strangely enough, my mother was all enthusiasm and gradually her high spirits infected me. Our home was the traditional log cabin of the pioneers, but unlike the cabins of early settlers, it had good insulation, air tight window frames and panes, and a cement foundation under the floor, so that we were warm and comfortable.

During the first week the women of the settlement held a house warming for us and brought all kinds of household goods including yards of red and white checked material for the tablecloths and kitchen curtains, a braided rug, a warm cozy quilt, and probably the most useful gift of all, a washboard. These women were of all different nationalities and each brought with her a favourite recipe. Italian spaghetti, macaroni and cheese, and Chili Con Carne were among the best. These women were so friendly that they became some of our firmest and fastest friends.

After the housewarming we had many things with which to fix up our little log cabin. We had one large room in the house and in it were combined living, dining, and cooking areas. It was the general room of the house, with bedrooms and a storeroom branching off. On the wide sanded boards of the floor we put a large round braided rug and on the windows were red and white checked curtains which matched the tablecloth. We soon got used to the inconvenience of a pump, wood-burning cook stove, and the extra work involved, and looked upon these things as an addition to the charm of the room. Willow-ware dishes in open cupboards, comfortable chairs, a sofa, and a rocking chair completed the picture. The books and papers which invariably got scattered around, a curly haired cocker spaniel sprawled behind the stove, and our pussycat curled up on the rocking chair, gave the place a homey, lived-in look.

Gardening was the women's work, so Mom and I faithfully planted and watered rows of vegetables, tended flower patches and built window boxes. Soon we were rewarded when small green sprouts crept unfolded in the white window boxes. I enjoyed fixing up our house and garden.

I wondered whether this was going to be all work and no play. As if to answer my question, I saw a bulletin in the station one day announcing a square dance which was to be held in the hall the following Saturday. News travels fast, and soon everyone in the camp was talking excitedly about the dance. Of course we were going, and even my two older brothers, who didn't dance much, were eagerly awaiting the event.

On Saturday night, every person in the camp flocked to the dance. The women and girls were dressed in full gingham skirts and peasant blouses, while the men and boys wore plaid shirts and blue jeans. The music was supplied by a fiddler and an accordian player who sat on bales of hay piled in one corner of the room. More bales placed around the edge of the hall provided seating space. Hay trailed down from the rafters and was piled in a stack in the middle of the floor. Light was provided by several oil lamps hung in the right places and there was warmth, friendliness, music and laughter from the floor to the rafters. When about half the dances were over, everyone was glad to rest and chat for a few minutes over delicious, heaping plates of baked beans. It was a wonderful dish to satisfy the hearty appetites of the strong, bronzed loggers and their families. When dancing was resumed, the couples promenaded and do-si-doed as energetically as they had in the beginning of the evening. Of course, every pleasant thing has to end sometime, and, just past midnight, so did this. As we drove away, the good-byes and good wishes of our new found friends followed us through the crisp frosty air and left a warm feeling in our hearts.

As I snuggled under the thick quilt on my bed that night, I thought about the people who had been at the dance. It had been my first chance to get really acquainted with the personalities which made a small camp like Greenwood such an interesting place. By far the most fascinating person there had been old Mrs. Sylvan, the headstrong woman who had been at Greenwood ever since the day it was formed in 1885. Although she was stone deaf, she had been doing square dances for so long that she knew every one of them perfectly and did not have to listen to the calls. During the intermission she had amused us all with stories of her journey across the prairies in a covered wagon and her train trip through the Rockies in the very earliest type of passenger car. Then there were the fifteen-year-old Longland twins, Jennie and Annie. They were true country girls. Strong and capable, they would someday make very good wives to a man who wanted a wife to stay at home, work hard, and be contented while doing so. Their features were quite ordinary but they were by no means ugly, and their hair, thick, dark and glossy, braided on top of the head, was most attractive. The only girl I met who was my own age, was Helga Svenson, a blond, blue eyed immigrant from Sweden. Although she had been in Canada for less than a year, her English was remarkably good, with few mistakes. She had impressed me as being the person I would like to have as my best friend. She had not been in Greenwood much longer than I, and we made plans to explore the woods and rivers together. Mr. Baruch and Mr. Dubois were two dapper Frenchmen who lived in the fanciest, most ornate house in Greenwood. They were the Beau Brummels of the camp, but they were good loggers and worked as hard and as long as anyone else. They became true Frenchmen, however, when they took off their rough clothes and donned smart pin-striped suits made by the best tailor in New York. Their abilities were very numerous. They could square dance, make wines and distil whisky, cook many exclusive French dishes, and they kept a litter of pigs which always took top honours at the country fairs.

These were the people who stood out most in my mind, but there were many others whom I was to meet later. I was too tired then to think about it, but I knew I enjoyed these kind of people, who were so different from Vancouverites.

One day, when the train came in, there appeared an extra attraction in the form of a salesman, who, to the amusement of all onlookers, went up to the station agent and asked where he could get a taxi to take him to a hotel. Upon finding that the train had left and that there was neither a hotel nor a taxi, his embarrassment increased and it was not helped by the stares and titters of the crowd. Quickly sensing his bewilderment, my mother, who sometimes lets her generosity rule her good sense, impulsively asked him to stay with us.

On the way home, however, we found that mother's decision had been a good one. The salesman, an Irishman named Michael Kilgallen, kept us all amused with his quick wit and good humour. Although he was rather odd in his ways, we liked him instantly. That evening was one of the most enjoyable we had ever known. After supper was finished and the dishes done, Mike spread his merchandise on the kitchen table, and as payment for his room and board, he allowed each of us to pick out our favourite item. This was quite difficult, as everything from cotton house dresses to the newest kind of hair oil came out of his bag. After we were all satisfied, he took out his fiddle and while he played, he sang in a clear tenor voice. Time passed unheeded, as folk songs, classical pieces, and popular tunes filled our cozy cabin with all of us joining in the choruses. When midnight came, Mike reluctantly put his fiddle away. Over steaming mugs of hot chocolate, we listened to stories of his native Ireland, about the shamrocks, leprechauns, and the blarney stone. As we exchanged good-nights and went to bed, I suddenly felt very happy and contented with this life. Michael left a few days later after selling much of his merchandise, and soon, much to our delight, a little wire-haired terrier arrived in a crate with a note which told us that it was from Mike. Now we are eagerly awaiting the day, soon we hope, when Mike will come and stay with us again.

It seemed as if everything that happened was pleasant and gave me a better opinion of the camp. I even loved school, which, when I had attended the airy, impersonal schools in Vancouver, I had loathed. Here, sitting in an old desk, well carved with initials, I felt as if I were visiting in someone's home. The teacher, Mr. Wallace, was a fascinating, robust, old man, who filled the pupils with knowledge, all the while making them feel as if they were enjoying themselves. There were only fifteen pupils, but the grades varied from grade one to grade eight. Everyone participated in the school activities which included spelling bees, singing, and concerts.

Corn roasts, quilting bees, taffy pulls, and gathering Christmas trees and evergreen boughs at Christmas time were all novelties to me, but they were an accepted part of Greenwood life made all the more enjoyable by the warm family spirit and the respect which children had for their elders. Indeed, this was not the dull, empty life I had expected when I first looked out the train window at Greenwood.

MARSHA HAYMAN,
British Columbia

TO A WILD HORSE

A noble creature made by God
To grace the face of earth,
Four shiny hooves to pound the sod
No saddle round this girth.

A coal black coat, a long-plumed tail,
Two ears alert and straight;
A mane windtossed by wind and gale
In sight no fence nor gate.

A rolling plain to roam at will,
A wild herd for his court
He rules supreme on moor and hill;
No need for roof or fort.

Janet Morris,
Alberta

ON TAKING HOME THE REPORT

It is an art. Even the finest acrobat or aircraft pilot cannot manoeuvre with the precision of the refined report 'taker-homer' which the student, by his years of experience, has developed. Who, but an artist, can hide from the eyes of a parent, the oblique bar between the 'C' and 'D'? What other profession than art has produced such a man as can explain that a 'D' is merely four letters away from 'A'? Even the object is a work of art. The kaleidoscope of the teacher's glowing crimson or eerie blue ink could be created only in the mind of an artist.

The expert, when taking home the report, does not tarry once the ill-fated card is in the home. Delay arouses suspicion in the mind of an already cynical father. The bearer of the card must approach with the confidence and courage of the lion. Only then can the suspicion of the wary 'daddy' be overcome. He must appear to be perplexed by the existing 'A' or 'B' to draw attention from the 'C' or 'D'. He must look modestly at the 'A' or 'B' and mention casually that he will do better at Easter. If the Latin teacher had used red ink which is luminous, the art of taking home a report becomes finer. The art becomes a strategy.

It is rumoured that Alexander the Great of Macedon learned his finest tactics because Aristotle used only blood-red ink on his note to Philip. The novice, if he is desperate enough, can put a red light-bulb in the lamp and hope that the father misses the red ink completely. This method is both crude and impractical. If all the teachers had used red ink, the parent might become somewhat suspicious of the seemingly blank report card. I can offer only sympathy for the student whose teachers love colour. The student is doomed. Even Alexander could not find a solution except to improve his marks.

Forgery is not recommended. Even the most uninterested parent could estimate a period of two months, at the end of which he expects to see the panorama of chaotic 'C's and 'D's. Besides, the sense of gallantry and fair play will undoubtedly overcome the student.

Three solutions are therefore offered to the student on taking home the report: admit defeat and be at the mercy of the father (or Father); improve your marks; or, break your father's glasses. Is it not odd that most mothers have twenty-twenty vision?

Jim Kadonaga,
Ontario

Some are lost and some survive,
Many to reach the sea will live.

THE LITTLE FIR TREE'S STORY

I am a little fir tree who is standing in a big earthen pot in a corner of a room in the orphanage. I would like to tell you my story but first you must understand that it is the dearest wish of all fir trees in the forest some day to become a Christmas tree to please the children of the world.

It was with pleasure that I listened to my grandfather telling of more fortunate trees and I stretched myself up in order that I might grow tall and handsome and be chosen for a Christmas tree, too. Perhaps, dreamed I, I might be placed in the square of some great city where more people than I had cousins would view me and be dressed out in so many beautiful lights that every twig could be seen.

One day in autumn when all the trees except for my family and myself, were beginning to look very bare, something happened that changed my whole life. The little stream on whose bank I grew, became a rushing torrent, swollen with extra rain water. Suddenly there was a shaking under my roots and the whole bank collapsed into the stream. I found myself being thrown against ragged rocks and whirled through the water at a dizzy rate. At length I was tossed into a quiet pool where the water was clear and shallow. "Oh, dear!" I sighed. "What will become of me now?" and I shed a few leaves for that is how fir trees cry.

Later that day, two children came running through the woods. When they saw me, the little boy wanted to break off my branches and play at being a sailor but the little girl who was kind and understanding, said, "Oh, no, Tommy. That would be cruel. I know of a way to have fun and be kind to the poor little tree. Let's pretend to be two of those men that look after the forest and plant the little tree again."

Luckily for me the little boy agreed to his sister's plan and very carefully they lifted me up and carried me to a pleasant spot among the trees.

Unfortunately the children did not know much about planting trees and my roots were bruised anyway. Although I bloomed through the four seasons like any other fir, I never grew any taller. How I envied the younger trees then. They would grow up and have a fair chance to become Christmas trees but no one wanted me — I was too small.

Another winter came around and as usual I was plunged in gloom. One day a young man came striding through the trees with an axe upon his shoulder and a merry tune upon his lips. When he saw me he stopped suddenly. "Why!" he exclaimed. "Fancy coming upon just the right kind of tree so soon. This is my lucky day."

"And this is mine," thought I as my heart nearly stopped beating for joy. (Fir trees have hearts, you know.) He easily lifted me right out of the ground, hoisted me onto his shoulder and off we went.

Now you can see how I got here. The children have a bigger tree out in the hall but they like me better for I am just the right size for the corner beside the warm hearth. I am very lucky for I bring joy to not one, but to many children who need me more than those who have homes and families of their own.

DIANE CORRIGAN,
Ontario

A CONVERSATION

Dew was gathering softly upon the thirsty ground in the cold quiet moment before dawn. A grey drop came to rest on an opening bud of a summer rose.

"Thank you, little dew-drop," said the rose-bud, contentedly. She opened her petals a little further, and carefully allowed her damp folds to dry in the brightening sun-light that grew in the east. As her full beauty emerged from the green case that had protected her, she grew more proud.

"Am I not beautiful?" she asked of the tiny dew-drop under her stem. "Do I not give great pleasure to those that behold me? I am surely far more useful than you."

The dew-drop, his task now over, exclaimed, "I do not think so, rose. Only a little while ago you were glad of the refreshment I was able to give you. If you are to give pleasure to the world, you must receive the care that my brothers and I can give you. Every morning you will look forward to our arrival. And not you alone receive our attention. See the grass blades, the new and tender shoots of green, your sisters also are glad to see us."

The rose shook herself angrily. "I am more beautiful than you, you drab fellow!" the rose exclaimed haughtily, for now long fingers of sun-beams were creeping to the remotest corners of the garden and were strengthening the young flowers.

"Beauty is of many kinds," replied the dew-drop weakly, for he felt himself growing smaller. "I have travelled much. I have raced in the wind over foam-flecked seas, and drifted lazily over meadows and gardens in the breast of the clouds. I have seen many things in my time of which you have no knowledge, young and foolish as you are. I have seen beauty in the graceful span of a suspension bridge; the beauty of a waterfall, water rushing over ragged rocks into the pool below with a mighty roar; the beauty of a thrush's song in early morning, the flight of a gull, trees in October, a garden after rain; there is beauty in love among people. Beauty is everywhere; it has only to be found."

As it spoke, a gentle breeze lifted the rose's head. A stray sun-beam struck the dew-drop and, for a moment, it hung sparkling and twinkling with a million different colours, reflecting the sun's gaiety in a rainbow pattern. Then, a sudden motion of the stem shook the dew-drop from its place.

DIANE CORRIGAN,
Ontario

PARTIE DE PECHE

Ah! qu'ils étaient beaux, les jours de mon enfance, passés à la pêche! Qu'ils étaient beaux les jours où, mon grand frère et moi, contemplions les reflets des vagues sur le beau lac St.-Jean, le sillage de la chaloupe, le village au loin.

Nous nous levions avec le soleil, et, après un frugal déjeuner, nous nous dirigions vers la cabane qui abritait la chaloupe, le moteur et les agrès de pêche. Une fois partis, les contours de la rivière nous apparaissaient, dans l'aurore qui jetait mille feux sur l'eau.

Il y avait, jusqu'aux deux ponts, celui de la route et celui du chemin de fer, de belles rives d'un vert atténué par la lumière naissante. De l'autre côté de ces ponts, notre joie commençait. C'était toujours comme si nous allions dans un autre monde, un monde de féeries. Une fois le chenal traversé, nous ouvrions notre route sur un lac immense qui s'étendait à perte de vue. Nous avancions toujours vers la pointe sablonneuse, dont la ouananiche faisait son lieu préféré.

Nous nous en allions, doucement bercés par les vagues mourantes, laissant derrière nous, les plages, les forêts, notre village.

Le soleil levant allumait d'innombrables fléchettes de feu, qui se jetaient dans nos yeux.

Nous passions le quai, les cabines, les chalets, où les Américains venaient l'été, nous émerveiller par leurs excentricités et leurs grosses voitures. Et nous arrivions enfin à la pointe. Le moteur à petite vitesse, nous laissions tranquillement nos lignes se dérouler au fil de l'eau.

Nous pouvions attendre parfois, des heures, sans prendre la plus petite perchaude. Pendant ces longues heures qui nous semblaient bien courtes pourtant, nous restions silencieux, d'un silence presque religieux, de peur de faire fuir le décor majestueux du matin. Mais, bon gré, mal gré, le paysage éclatant de l'aurore, s'émoussait, petit-à-petit et bientôt, un disque de feu nous brûlait l'épiderme.

La plupart du temps, ces heures étaient perdues, quand nous rentrions bredouille. Mais non! ces heures n'étaient pas perdues. Pour nous, toujours, elles étaient des enchantements sans nom, dans lesquels nos yeux puisaient d'insondables trésors de beauté et de décors pittoresques. Elles étaient pour notre coeur, un renouveau de gaieté et de bonheur.

Nous étions remplis d'un orgueil bien légitime, en pensant que pas une force au monde, ne saurait détruire une oeuvre de la nature d'une telle splendeur. Vraiment ici sur terre, peut-il y avoir joies si sublimes, si pures, que celles, puisées dans la belle nature de Dieu?

REMI PLOURDE,
Québec

THE TRAIL

Calm, rippled only gently,
The lake lies
Beneath the red ball of fire
Sinking in the west;
Placid, still. Upon a trail of fire
Across its shimmering surface
Glides a green canoe.
Straight into the setting sun
It sets its course;
Two dark figures etched against the sky,
Paddles slipping in and out together.
In at the West Wind's gate it softly goes;
Eyes are dazzled, then the sun slips down
Behind the purple hills, and it is gone.

ANNE C. BEGOR,
Quebec

A SHROPSHIRE EXPERIENCE

We had had a tiring day and must have covered about fifteen miles on foot. As evening cast its long shadows across the countryside we approached a village of thatched cottages from which twinkled the first welcoming lights of evening.

On the outskirts of the hamlet we paused for a moment. After a hurried discussion we decided to stay here for the night. The village was conveniently placed and so with tired legs we set out to find a place to sleep.

Situated in the middle of the village was a comfortable, little building which proclaimed itself to be 'The Traveller's Rest'. We decided to try it.

A motherly-looking lady admitted us and, upon hearing our request, gave us a room on the top floor, telling us that she would have a meal ready for us in a few minutes. Then we prepared to settle down and enjoy our hospitable surroundings.

We withdrew to the front room after setting out our skeleton baggage and eating a greatly-desired meal. It was here that we met the husband of our hostess and the owner of the inn. He told us how we might make the most of this country through which we were journeying. He showed us maps of the district around and routes we could take. Then he led us into another room and asked us to light our pipes.

The old man must have spent his entire life collecting. Around the walls, neatly arranged, was an array of antiques, weapons both modern and historical, and many, many oddments such as I had never seen before. There were death masks, old flintlocks and muskets, yellow documents, musty with age, African spears and shields, old china and specimens of rock that would have made geologists turn green with envy. And into his collection the old man seemed to fit like the first exhibit.

He invited us to sit down and offered us some whisky, which we declined. After a few remarks about his collection, he launched into such stories as I shall never hear again. In his soft Shropshire dialect he recounted to us tales of his own home and family. His stories began hundreds of years ago and told about his own people and how they lived in days gone by. Every few minutes he would indicate one of the objects on the shelves to illustrate his accounts. Interwoven with his story was the history of that part of England for the past thousand years. He related how his people had been woodcarvers until their custom began to drop away and his great-grandfather had abandoned the once-flourishing trade.

He had collected, he said, this assortment of antiques through years of unceasing work. They had been handed down through his family — souvenirs of toil and hardship each telling a story of its own. People had stayed at his hostel who had either left these queer objects as payment (for they were more valuable to the old man than all the money in the world) or had forgotten them as they hurried on their way.

I had never spent such an evening as this. His voice flowed along and time became obliterated. It was almost sunrise when we went up to our rooms. After a hurried breakfast (at eleven o'clock!) we were off again to see more of the country about which we now felt we knew so much.

I shall never forget that memorable night. My companion, too, was deeply impressed. We often meet at night and go over the events of that fascinating evening.

Neither of us have ever gone back to where the old man sits in his armchair, puffing at his pipe, recounting his stories to others, in the midst of his collection of antiques. We do not intend to. But in our minds the experiences of our visit will live as though they were happening every day.

Gerald Wright,
Ontario

A WARRIOR'S RETURN

Slowly, as if in a dream, he turned in at the rusty, sagging gate. Pushing back his battered grey hat, he tilted his head to peer down the long avenue of trees that marked the beginning of his father's estate. Was the place still there? Through the dimness of the early twilight, he could faintly discern the white structure.

But it was no longer the proud sentinel of a vanished civilization. For its roof was sagging, its pillars crooked and its windows broken. But it was still alive. With mounting excitement, he clucked to his horse, swiftly mounting the hill with new found energy.

Nothing replied to his first feverish shouts but an echo down the long, endless corridors. He had half-heartedly expected the girls to come any minute, blushing, as of old. But as before, there was nothing. Only the eerie stillness of time past.

Heart beating, he strode to his mother's little office, where, in better times, she had attended to the affairs of a thriving plantation. But there was nothing. No rustle of her skirt, as she rose from the tiny chair at her desk, no hand lightly patting his cheeks in passing, no scent of lemon verbena that he loved. Only a dry and yellow piece of paper dated 1864, lying on the mantelpiece. A few months ago they had evacuated to Savannah, when the fighting had come too close. Yankees here, at Heather Hill?

As if in a daze, he wandered from the office, into the immense, circular hall that ran from back to front of the house. He stood on the cut marble floor which his father had imported from Italy years before, and stared blankly at the ruined stairs where twilight peeped through from a break in the ceiling. The mahogany bannisters dangled from the top parapet like some huge, dead snake, while the stairs themselves were crumpled and broken. Above him the crystal chandelier hung dust-ridden and silent like some little sun that had ceased to shine.

Bitterly, he thought how wrong they had all been. Back, as if in another world, he remembered the wild shouts and shining eyes that had accompanied the playing of *Dixie* and the beginning of it all. Oh yes, it had been easy then to talk of marching bravely off to War. When surrounded by that golden warmth of life, not winning was ridiculous. But, that was all over now. Finished. Turning towards the back of the house, he passed the quaint little drawing-room of his mother's. The room was bare – the marauding Yankees had left nothing in their plundering haste. Perhaps because it was too heavy, they had left the portrait of his grandfather, an immense old gentleman with a flowing-white beard and hickory cane. The portrait had been scarred by some Northern Soldier's bayonet.

He turned on his heel, and headed for the rear of the house. He felt he must get some air.

Vaguely outlined against the mauve sky, he could see the charred skeletons of the now silent negro cabins. This filled him with a painful nostalgia. He could never give up all this . . . the rolling, red hills, the softly swaying pines, the long drowsy days under a juniper bush, lying in the thick, green verdure with the bees buzzing in the flowers overhead. For a moment he heard, or thought he heard wafted on the faint breeze the songs of the darkies, as they drifted homewards at day's end, from the cotton-fields.

But, it was only a notion from the faraway past. No, it was more than a notion, it was a link. A link with the old days – with what was gone.

This blood-red earth would give him strength and courage to face the future and to forget what was behind him. Out of the futility of life, and the chores, here was a glimmer of hope. This hope would lead him, and the rest of the South to rise above the backwardness and decay.

He breathed in deeply the warm, scented air, placed his hands on the porch rail, and looked out across the darkening horizon.

But somehow, the warmth had gone out of it.

D. J. Parsons,
Ontario

TWISTED ROOTS

CHARACTERS:

Farmer — small, stooped and wizened . . . a persistent pessimist and a sadist.

Edgar — feeble-minded, helpless and apparently harmless, large, awkward, and big-boned.

CURTAINS OPEN:

A combination of various lights including green makes a dream-like shimmering quality on stage — changing gradually into a red light bathing the set. The set is nightmare-like with an old weather beaten barn slightly cockeyed in shape and tipping to one side as the main figure. A gnarled and twisted tree stands SR with the body leaning downward to the ground. Dead lifeless leaves hang from its limbs and lie strewn around it. A vaguely beaten path leads from offstage L and runs right up to the barn door.

There is no definite time, but a quality of time-stopped should be created. Perhaps instead of a moon suspended in sky, there could be a clock with large deformed hands hanging lifelessly down.

Farmer enters SL carrying a spade over his shoulder. He is bent almost as crooked as the tree and grumbles to himself in time to his quick shuffling steps. The gawky helper follows slowly in after him with a vacant expressionless look on his large features.

FARMER: *(advancing and speaking in time to his steps)*
Work, work, always work,
Rise at dawn, plough the field,
Work, work, a measly yield.
Found a stranger in the loft
Stiffened corpse, useless tramp,
Foolish bother, night is damp.
(he lets some soil slip through his fingers, rubs it ecstatically)

Work, work, always work,
Fuss, fuss, always fuss.
Let him rot to devil's mound . . .
What care I? . . . six feet of ground . . .
(shovelling dirt on grave in time to words)

Work, work, always work.
Where's the fool? Come here, you lout.
Your fiendish soul I'll put to rout.
(brandishes spade at him, and laughs sadistically as moron stumbles back in fear)
My sister's child, 'helps' me here,
(swings around suddenly on this line and leers at audience)
Saved him from them doctors there.
Ungrateful wretch, empty head,
Fuss and bother, must be fed.

Work, work, always work
(kicks grave spitefully—a faint rumble in background)
Still grumbling he moves off SR.
(staring stupidly down at grave, Edgar, slowly and with effort says):
"Rest in Peace."

Slowly covers whole stage looking for farmer. Movements are dull and pondered, in direct contrast to farmer's quick steps. Crosses to SR and with great expectation on face reaches into pocket. Drawing in breath he pulls out a glittering necklace. (Speech is slow and thick, almost childlike.)

Edgar: Pretty, pretty . . . mine.

All for Edgar . . . yes.
Put them on now . . . see.

One, two, three.
Many, many, agates.
He'll not have them – no.
(looks offstage after farmer in fear and hugs necklace lovingly)
He would want to hurt them,
Scratch them, break them, beat them.
(small crescendo in speed)

Pretty, pretty . . . mine.
(falls back to original tone)
All for Edgar . . . yes.
Found you in the hay,
Near the stranger lay.
Stranger gave to Edgar,
Smiled and said, "for Edgar".
He not laugh at Edgar.
Edgar love him . . . yes.
Pretty, pretty . . . mine.

Something for Edgar.
(change of beat; on these lines he breaks into a weird ungainly dance, holding necklace under single spotlight SR, and blinking delightedly at result)
Necklace for Edgar.
Shiny for Edgar.

Shine in the sunlight
Here in the sunlight
That visits this barnyard
So seldomly.
Twinkle and smile,
Laugh all the while
At Edgar's fond love
From which they all flee.

Something for Edgar.
Necklace for Edgar.
Pretty for Edgar.

Farmer: *(Enters with quickened gait)*
Work, work always work,
Where's that boy? Stupid waste
Fuss and bother, come in haste . . . *(to moron)*
Fuss, fuss, always fuss,
Hurry, lout, day is done,
Night winds howl, no work begun.

But stand here now, what have you there?
Ah see, the poor fool cowers o'er
To cover mine and of mine sweat.
Some bread or cornmeal do you hide?
His eyes from mine in guilt do slide *(to himself)*
Ah, sparkle, sparkle, peeps there out
Like golden wheat on shimmering stalk,
Like golden coins they smile and mock.
(tone lowers greedily)

Work, work, always work.
Nought to show, an aching back.
The help of God is what I lack.
(shakes fist at glowering sky)
All wicked joy for us I shun,
Two meals a day, a roof above,
And work, work, I hate and love.
It draws me like the fiend from Hell,
I fight and twist and then succumb,
Till bones and mind and soul are numb.
Have pity, boy, for you are well.
(given special emphasis)

Come now, son, what have you there?
My kindness now deserves reward.
(honeyed pleading. He reaches out and accidentally touches grave. His face changes into a personification of greed.)

A green light slowly grows over stage

Heed me, child, your father pleads,
My love for you exceeds my needs.
I will it hold for thy future use
So give it me, or earn abuse.
(last part almost growled as his grasping hands reach out closing and unclosing in frustration)

Fuss, fuss, always fuss.
You clumsy oaf, no help are here *(almost screaming)*
Charity calls, then I appear.
Repay, repay, my lifelong work.
That bauble, trinket, shall be mine.
Or damned in Hell, my soul and thine.

Edgar: Necklace for Edgar,
Pretty for Edgar,
Always you want
Always you take
(build crescendo through this passage—both tone and speed)
Squirrel for Edgar
Kitty for Edgar
Something to love
For helplessness sake.
Always you want
Always you take,
Take it and hurt it
And finally break.

Take it from Edgar — *(touches grave) . . . rumble*
Have it from Edgar — *(advances toward farmer, no longer the harmless fool)*

FARMER: *(Somewhat frightened)*
Fuss, fuss always fuss.
Work, work, always work,
Things to be done, wheat to be reaped,
Here now, boy, your food shall be heaped.
Stay now, lout, hold your hand *(effort of boldness)*
Edgar, Edgar . . . *(cry)*

Necklace is wrapped around farmer's neck and breaks, spilling over whole stage. Farmer falls back over grave, with eyes staring up at Edgar.
Edgar stands at full height above farmer, and cries out wildly, almost exultantly, with arms raised. He is no longer stooped and harmless in appearance.

EDGAR: Pretty, pretty, mine,
Sparkle, sparkle, shine.
At last he's fallen, lo — *(triumphant)*
Farmer, farmer, oooh —
(now horror creeps into his voice as he gazes at his huge hands wonder struck. At end of line he falls before grave sobbing pitifully)
They are staring at Edgar, *(referring to glittering beads)*
Glaring at Edgar,
Shining and blinking
And winking at Edgar.

Edgar is sorry,
work to be done . . . *(to farmer)*
Hurry, old farmer,

Come on the run. *(pleading)*
I'll plough the field
Mend the share,
And nary a grumble
Will give you a care.

Poor old farmer — *(slowly realizes farmer is dead — drops head in hands in despair)*
Wicked old farmer,
Why did he hurt me
And hate me so?
Was he afraid
Of what he was made?
To see and admit
'twas from him that I grow.
(during this and the following speech he is no longer the moron, but stands as a man)

I am his harvest,
His lifelong harvest.
What I am now
He has forged with his hand.
Sowed he the seed
Of my simple breed,
Then laughed at himself
In the form of my stand.
(once again he becomes desperately terrified)
They are staring at Edgar,
Glaring at Edgar,
LAUGHING and blinking
And winking at Edgar.
Always they watch
Eyes all around
Always I feel
But hear not a sound.

Why do you peer?
(swings sharply around to point finger at audience)
Add to my fear?
Cover your eyes,
FOR I AM YOU.

He gradually sinks into a huddled ball of misery. Then the shaking of his shoulders subsides slowly, and once again the moron, he becomes entranced by a bead. His hand creeps hesitatingly out from his form and grasps it. Gazing at it raptly, he speaks in a very childlike and slow manner, like his first speech.

Pretty, pretty . . . mine.
All for Edgar . . . yes.

Stage lights cast a flickering dream-like quality once again — gradual fadeout, — and curtains closed. . . . More extensive lighting, sound, character studies and costuming left to discretion of director.

BEVERLEY ROSEN,
Alberta

MY PAL AND I

Down on the bank beside the brook
Or up on the hill, against the sky,
Here we go to our favourite nook,
My pal and I.

All day long in the golden sun,
Watching the clouds go rolling by,
Wandering the trails 'til day is done,
My pal and I.

CHARLOTTE G. HALDENBY,
Yukon

FINAL ASSIGNMENT

I always knew the time would come when I would get my final assignment, but I never thought it would be like this.

My mind flashed back over all those other assignments, none of them easy; some had really had me in a tight corner.

I thought of the 'Dangers of the Deep' – in search of sunken treasure on the ocean floor, trapped in a diving suit with the air line cut off by the tentacles of a giant devil-fish. I had come through that one successfully; but that was not the last.

My mind passed too, to the Phantom Clipper story, and the hair rose again on the back of my neck at the memory of a full-rigged sailing vessel looming out of the foggy seas, outlined in an eerie glow. And in retrospect again I awoke on my leafy bed of palm leaves to find myself a lone survivor 'Wrecked on a Tropical Island'.

Yes, there had been many and varied assignments, each presenting its own difficulties and obstacles to be overcome, but all eventually checked off 'Assignment Completed'.

My mind is cloudy and my brow is furrowed as I reluctantly force my unwilling thoughts back to the present. It must be faced; this is in the present and time is moving relentlessly on. A feeling of urgency rises within me, and I know I must make my plan and carry it through as best I may. The final outcome is in the lap of fate, and I have had my share of good fortune.

Think then and plan; no more of this indecision; let action take the place of hesitation.

With deep foreboding I draw a paper towards me, I take my pen in hand, and resolutely I begin. But . . . stay! This is not the beginning; this is the end – the end of my final assignment.

FRANCES GRIFFITHS,
Ontario

A LIBERAL-MINDED PERSON

Politics are very important in our family. Dad has always been and always will be a Liberal backer providing their tactics coincide with his. I don't see how our government ever survived the early days before Dad was born unless it was solely through his forefathers' efforts.

Every morning at breakfast Dad turns to the political page in the morning paper, reads through the whole paper in silence and then proceeds to eat his breakfast. It is not until his second cup of coffee that he begins to either run down or support the government's fumbling efforts. For instance, a few weeks ago when the Minister of Fisheries, Gordon Sinclair, visited Russia and slipped and broke his ankle as well as misplacing a vertebra (although I don't see how anyone could misplace vertebrae) my father got highly indignant over Mr. Sinclair's visit or, as he put it, "Darn fool, off runnin' around in Russia. Probably he and Mr. Khrushchev were off fishin' when he broke his ankle. Now we'll be expected to pay his hospital bill." Dad was full of ideas of how if Mr. Sinclair had stayed home and seen to it that his (Dad's) favourite trout stream had been amply stocked with ten-inch Brook Trout then Mr. Sinclair would never have broken his ankle and worse still would never have lost Dad's support. For now Dad was going to insure himself some good fishing in his old age. Dad is going to vote Social Credit, that is until they do something he doesn't agree with.

Dad had finally and positively decided to become a Social Credit backer. At home or at the office he was telling everybody how great the Social Credit party was and how much better it was going to become now that he had decided to give his wholehearted support to the party. This went on for a week until someone innocently asked him, "Now that you're on such good terms with the Social Credit party, just what was the idea of that election last spring?" Dad was stumped but rather than admit it he told him that he would have the information for him in a few days.

When he got home that night he started to think pretty seriously about that question and just why did they have that election?

The more he thought about it the less enthused he grew over giving his support to the party. After all, wasn't it a Liberal who was in there demanding to know the facts about the government's business dealings? "Yes, sir, those Liberals aren't so slow; they know when there's something fishy in governmental affairs." These and other remarks soon gave me the impression that Dad was not a Social Crediter after all but a Liberal in Social Credit clothing going around seeing just who was a Loyal Liberal and who was a Sneaky Social Crediter. Apparently Dad was gathering a list of all Social Crediters who should be shot just as soon as the Liberals with the aid of Dad, of course, took over any and all Social Credit offices.

Dad now goes to work with his coat collar up, his hat brim down and a crafty gleam in his eyes, just waiting for someone to slip and state he's anything but a Liberal and down goes his name into Dad's mental black book. Yes, Dad always has been and always will be a Liberal.

ALLAN MACRAE,
Alberta

LAMENT FOR A CAN OF SALMON

O salmon, stored upon the shelf,
I'll bet you hardly know yourself,
Stripped of your scales and bony fins
Your future life confined to tins.

You tasty morsel from the sea,
Were once a minnow, young and free,
Why should you, O my scaly friend,
In a sandwich meet your end?

PHIL WILSON,
British Columbia

A CANADIAN HEROINE

In the darkness of a cold, wind-swept night, the figure of a small girl battled against the waves of Lake Ontario. She struggled for twenty-one long hours, and covered a distance of forty miles to bring outstanding honour to Canada. This is why Marilyn Bell is the heroine I should like to meet.

Eight weeks before, this young schoolgirl had completed a twenty-five mile swim off Atlantic City, the only woman to finish this marathon. Canada did not recognize her feat, so Marilyn went unnoticed. But on the ninth of September when she swam from Youngstown, New York, to the Sunnyside breakwater in Toronto, the name of Marilyn Bell became known to the entire world.

Her start did not command widespread attention because all eyes were focused on Florence Chadwick, the thirty-four-year-old American, considered by many to be the world's greatest woman swimmer. She had been brought by the Canadian National Exhibition officials as a feature attraction, and had been promised a purse of ten thousand dollars if she completed the swim. Marilyn and another Canadian swimmer, without offer of reward, followed Miss Chadwick into the lake.

Many hours after the start Miss Chadwick and Mrs. Leuszler were lifted exhausted from the water, leaving the plucky youngster to carry on alone. Several times she reached the point of exhaustion, and pleaded to be taken out, but her trainer urged her on until it became apparent that she was going to attain her goal.

As the word began to spread, eager spectators crowded the shoreline, rival newspapers fought with one another, Canadian National Exhibition officials changed their minds and offered monetary rewards and admirers pledged gifts. As the tiny hand of the courageous swimmer reached out to touch the sea-wall and victory, the dramatic news of her conquest was flashed to a waiting world.

I was challenged and fascinated by the fact that a fellow Canadian teen-ager had brought fame and goodwill to her country. I should like to meet this young heroine because from her pictures and press reports I believe she is a very likeable girl, and that we would have many interests in common. Her swim has revealed the qualities of patience, courage and perseverance. These qualities I admire.

NANCY JANE SMITH,
Quebec

THE HUNTED

Now the darkness and the light
Mingle together; 'twill soon be night.
All around, the earth grows still,
Even mottled whippoorwill
Closes his beak. The foxes sleep
Quite unaware that chickens cheep
Not far away. Rest undisturbed,
This night is peace, no sound is heard.

But suddenly upon the ear
There comes a sound wild creatures fear—
The sound of man conversing loud
With his companions, there is a crowd.
They have their guns; they're out to kill;
What happens now to whippoorwill
And sly red fox? They'll lead a chase,
But in the end man wins the race.

DORIS MOSS,
Newfoundland

ON HANDSHAKES

Hear the crunching of a bone, or the resounding echo of a clamorous slap? Well, this just might be an expression of a greeting. Someone who had been in my presence only several days before, attacks me from behind with a healthy whack on the back, accompanied by a deafening yell, "How are you? Haven't seen you in a dog's age!" That's more than enough for anyone. Then there's that someone who offers me a hand so limp that it feels like the hand of a rag-doll, rather than a human. Or, sometimes they like to surprise me by looking frail and helpless, but their handshake turns out to be a vice-like grip on me. And my poor crumpled hand is useless for days afterwards! There are others who attempted to shake my hand with great pumping gestures. I am convinced that they must have owned a well sometime; or else, where on earth did they learn that pumping routine so perfectly?

Amid slapping and pumping, you might find someone with an enjoyable handshake. The other day I met such a person. Unbelievable, isn't it? Well, I was overwhelmed as I never dreamed I'd ever encounter such a one. Speechless, I nodded my greeting.

Mary Bahrich,
Saskatchewan

OUR ENGLISH LANGUAGE

Enough will rhyme with tough
But rough won't rhyme with bough
Dough will rhyme with though
But what will rhyme with plough?

Cough will rhyme with trough
But through won't rhyme with though
And so it is no wonder
That poets crazy gough.

GAIL PATTON,
Ontario

LA CITÉ DES HOMMES

Les hommes ont construit une ville.
Et ils appelèrent la ville
Du nom de leur nudité: NÉANT.

Les hommes ont construit une ville.
Et ils tracèrent des plans;
Des plans avec des angles,
Des chiffres et des signes;
Des plans avec des lignes,
Des courbes et des points;
Des plans avec des calculs,
Des nombres et des numéros.

Les hommes ont construit une ville.
Et les plans qu'ils avaient tracés
Etaient beaux et grands.
Seulement, les plans avaient oublié,
Et les hommes avec eux avaient oublié
Les hommes.

Il y avait place pour les rues,
Les maisons et les usines,
Mais pas de place pour les hommes. . . .

Les hommes ont construit une ville.
Du béton et de l'acier.
Une ville de leur chair
Et de leurs doigts écrasés sous le marteau.
Une ville où les vies
Du roc, de l'arbre, de l'homme
Se déchirent et se broient
Dans un magnifique trio de mort.

Les hommes ont construit une ville.
Et ils appelèrent la ville
Du nom de leur nudité: NÉANT.

Michel Barcelo,
Québec

RED WHITE AND BLUE

Through the grey light of dawn the wind and snow blew over the frozen ground. About sixty miles from Rosthern stood a still figure in the snow, a man on a horse, as still and colourless as the surroundings. The horse was a snow white stallion, neither large nor small, but built for speed. The only dark colour on him was his eyes. The white leather saddle and bridle with the silver bit could hardly be seen. The rider was nearly as colourless as his horse. His hair, although he was still young, was white, and his skin was rather blue from the cold. His eyes were a very pale mauve and he wore a cougar skin coat and blue jeans. His boots were black rubber and there was a roll of blankets on the back of the saddle. Like a shadow left by the departed night, a gaunt grey timber wolf followed at the horse's heels. The horse turned his head and walked on to the south.

When they arrived at the Lilly L. Ranch, the owner, Jim Bradford, sat with his two children in the kitchen. Mr. Bradford was mixing some mash for a horse and sent the two children to the door. Dan, twelve, was dressed in pyjamas and a sheepskin. Sally, two years younger, was dressed in pyjamas and a bear-skin coat. Dan opened the door, and for two minutes stood staring. The party on the outside stared also, and with good reason. Dan judged the man to be about twenty-five and the horse about four years old.

"I would like to help on this ranch here, to get a bit of hay for my horse. What about it?"

"Come in," answered Sally, "and ask Daddy about it."

He dismounted and left the horse and wolf together.

"So you want to work here," said Mr. Bradford, having used his ears to good advantage. "What about this horse and wolf of yours?"

"Well," began the stranger, "the horse is Platinum, stronger and whiter than silver, and worth more than gold." Here he paused with a grin. "And the wolf is Timber."

Mr. Bradford looked carefully at the young man. "Go get him some breakfast, Sally," said he.

After breakfast Mr. Bradford told him about Ghost Valley, in which they had been losing cattle, and into which their horses refused to go, and they dared not go on foot. They rode out to it and Timber and Platinum entered without fear. They came to a camp where two men froze at the sight of the three.

"What are you doing here?" gasped one.

"Get going and never mind," said the stranger, drawing a gun. The gun and Timber helped them go peacefully to jail.

The stranger continued to work at the ranch for several weeks.

"That albino isn't so bad," said Mr. Bradford, "and what a horse!"

One morning Platinum was missing. As his owner did not appear worried, no one said anything.

Three days later Platinum returned with some scars and sixteen red bay mares. They were a band of fine horses which the Bradfords had been trying to catch for some time. Only Platinum knew what had become of the pinto stallion which had been with them, and, no doubt, he was responsible.

"Why did the stallion come back now?" asked Mr. Bradford.

"To get me," said the stranger. "He is afraid without me."

The young man sat astride Platinum, the blankets again on the back of the saddle. Mr. Bradford noted this in silence.

"But how can he be afraid?" he persisted.

"Goodbye," was the only answer.

That night, about thirty miles away, in their camp, the strange trio stood in the moonlight, looking at the sixteen red mares on the white snow, under the blue night sky.

Delphine McKenzie,
British Columbia

IT CAN'T HAPPEN HERE

When Old Jim awoke he felt different. He stretched his old aching joints, yawned and glanced at the alarm clock on his night table. Its face meant nothing to him. "Well, blow me over!" thought Jim, shutting his eyes in the hope that when he opened them this time, he would be able to tell the time. Jim sat bolt upright in bed, now thoroughly alarmed. "Good night," he thought, "is the world coming to an end?" Quickly he scrambled out of bed and grabbed his Bible; for Jim was a God-fearing man. Quickly he opened it with trembling fingers. Frantically he whipped the rustling pages back and forth in a nervous frenzy, but all that stared back at him was a jumbled mass of marks. Dumbly he stared down at the meaningless jumble of symbols. The tragic truth dawned on him, he Jim Johnson, could no longer read or write.

Old Jim paced back and forth across the bedroom floor. As he passed his night table for the hundredth time he stopped short, a look of unbelief, then relief flooding his face. A faint flicker of a smile crept onto the gaunt old face. A deep chuckle started down at the bottom of his throat and ended up a rollicking laugh. In fact, Old Jim was laughing so hard he had to sit down.

"Why . . . why what an old fool I am getting to be!" he thought. "Why, I can't even remember to put my glasses on."

Happily Old Jim reached for his gold rimmed spectacles, perched them on the end of his nose, and contentedly began to read his Bible.

WAYNE CRANSTON,
Ontario

ON LITERARY WORKS

Long ago in England one of my ancestorial cousins twice removed got hisself in a little mix up in a bar. Now don't you go athinkin' this was natural. Why Chris never ever drank more'n but social. But as the story goes he was kelled in that brawl and me bein' a Marlowe, or Marleau (as the case may be) to the core, I ups and reads back the minutes of the previous history.

It was like I figured, no kin o' mine would git hisself killed in any two-bit bar. He'd of hired a hotel room.

Well further in this story I finds out he skips across that itybity stream to France. To further disguise hisself, he changes his name to Marleau and marries a debutante of fine rich French blood. (It is sometime later afore I gits into things.)

Now while he is in France wine women and singing his unhappy hours of exile away, he writes a number of plays, under the nom de plume of William Shakespeare. He even goes so far as to git a stand-in of the same name.

But Chris underestimated the intelligence of this man 'quivering arrow'. He swindled Chris out of authorship and takes all the glory (those devilish English!).

Cuz realized he was a defeated man, but, wanting his work recognized, played heavily on a lot of tear jerking sonnets, which he continued to turn over to the swindling knave.

In reality he was relying on one of his future ancestors to rescue his disgrace.

Now Chris I want you to rest yerself and quit flippin' about yer grave. I'm here to do just that, just you wait and see.

Bacon did not write those plays; Anne Hathaway did not write those plays; PUBLIC NOTICE – I wrote them plays.

See, Chris, ya cain't even trust yer own kin, kin ya?

To prove I wrote those plays, analyze this line from one of my famous plays, 'The Dog and the Fox'.

"The quick brown fox jumps over the lazy dog."

Take the third letter of the fifth word, the second letter of the eighth word, the last letter of the sixth word, the first letter of the eighth word, the last letter of the first word, leave a blank, add the second letter of the second word, pause – first word.

Now take the fourth, second and third letters of the third word (in that order), now add the first and last letters of the seventh word, pause – end of second word.

Take the last letter of the fifth word, the middle letter of the seventh word, leave a . . . add the last letter of the second word, the third letter of the sixth word, leave a . . . add the fourth letter of the fifth word, leave three . . . and add 'e', the missing letters are 'a' – 'a', – 's' – 'e' – 'a' – 'r', in that order.

Simple really, all it takes is hours. See you at my next production: I'll be producing another of my great plays under the nom de plume of George Bernard Shaw.

Annette Marleau,
British Columbia

THE STRANGER

Mrs. Toller, a plump middle-aged woman with greying hair and dark brown eyes, was sitting in a rocking chair on her front veranda drinking iced tea when she saw a tall young man with horn rimmed glasses knock on Mrs. Drake's door.

"Mrs. Drake isn't home," she called, standing up to enable the young man to see who was addressing him. "She went down to the butcher's to buy some meat for supper but she should be back in a few minutes. Come and drink some iced tea with me and wait for her."

The stranger strode through the white wooden gate, sat down on the other rocking chair, and watched a mother robin feed her little ones. He could hear Mrs. Toller getting him the iced tea in the kitchen.

"Here you are," smiled Mrs. Toller handing him a tall glass and sitting comfortably in her rocking chair, before she explained, "My husband is finished work at three o'clock and on warm days like this I always have some iced tea or fruit juice to refresh him. He should be home any minute now."

"Thank you," nodded the man. "It is very kind of you to invite me over. Where did you say Mrs. Drake was?"

"She's expecting the new minister for supper tonight; she went to the butcher's for some meat," Mrs. Toller repeated before going into the kitchen to take a lemon pie out of the oven, and calling through the open kitchen window, "We are all so sorry to see Reverend Lewis, our former minister, retire because we know this young minister who is coming on the afternoon train will never be as good."

Startled by what she had told him, Mr. Armstrong was quiet for some time before he asked, "Why did all the people like Reverend Lewis so well."

Rocking back and forth in her rocking chair, and sipping the cold drink, Mrs. Toller thought a while before she answered. "His sermons weren't very good, but he did have a pleasant personality. He only visited on Mondays and Thursdays so we didn't have to worry about his walking in when we were baking or scrubbing the floor. Often he phoned before coming to enable us to comb our hair and tidy the house."

"How was he able to visit all his congregation?" questioned Mr. Armstrong, looking as if his head was aching from doing mental calculations.

"Oh, it wasn't hard," remarked Mrs. Toller as she finished her drink and set the glass on the floor. "Some people who went to church before Mr. Lewis came stopped coming, so the congregation isn't very big. Most of those people thought they were too good for us anyway, but I suppose they will come back to church to hear this new minister and his new ideas." She sat looking at the floor as if it would tell her this statement was not true.

Mr. Armstrong stared queerly for a minute before he asked, "Is that your husband now?" And he pointed to a tall man with big shoulders getting out of a light blue Pontiac.

"Yes," Mrs. Toller stated and waved gaily to the approaching figure. "Come and meet Mr. Armstrong. He's new in town and I've been telling him about the new minister."

"How do you do?" greeted Mr. Toller as he shook hands with Mr. Armstrong. "Are you working at the factory?"

"No, I'm the new minister."

BETTY ANDERSON,
Ontario

OUR FARM

On our farm, so large and fair,
No machinery or buildings rattle.
No tottering hide-bound ghosts are there,
Nothing but Axford's cattle.

BARRY AXFORD,
Saskatchewan

ON BEING A DOCTOR'S DAUGHTER

Who could possibly be better suited to relate the experiences of living in a doctor's household than the doctor's daughter, herself?

The telephone rings, a marvellous invention by Alexander Graham Bell, or at least it has been thought so by all members of the human race, except doctors, who never fail to say, "and to think they erect monuments to the etc. etc.!!" (Doctors can not be held responsible for their language when the telephone rings at three o'clock in the morning). The whole household is awakened, including the dog and the bird, and there are some soft, but decidedly angry mutterings coming from the doctor's room. Poor Mom is always saying: "Temper, temper! Now be patient!" But she also has a queer gleam in her eye, for she too will spend a sleepless night. The doctor finally makes it to his car, muttering all the way, and backs out of the driveway with a bang, invariably missing the tree by an eighth of an inch. At last he is off, and we all go back to sleep, sadly pitying the poor nurses who will have to listen to his mad rantings.

"Someone's dying! Doctor come quickly!" Father is urged to go (I might say 'made to go'). Much later he returns home with murder in his eye. At breakfast we ask, "What was it? Who died?" His response? "It was only a drunk!" Need I add that we all stay clear of him for the next twelve hours?

Most people are under the false impression that an M.D.'s family gets the best medical attention possible. Now – that is the greatest understatement of the century. You are not supposed to get sick in a doctor's home. It is absolutely against the rules, and if you do, you might just as well pick out your niche at the local cemetery, step into your coffin, pull down the lid, fold your hands, and wait for St. Peter – for all the attention you will get. He is far too busy with appendectomies, perforated ulcers, pancreatid-idies, gall-bladders and leaky valves to bother about such simple things as family ailments. "Go and see a doctor," is his stock in trade answer to all your ills!

Doctor's children are rather odd creatures, born to the smell of ether, nurtured on Ostogen A with C, and all vitamins from A to Z (free samples, too!). They cut their first teeth on their fathers' stethoscopes and instead of nursery rhymes, recite such words as: stethoscopes, forceps, scissors and scalpels, Penicillin, Streptomycin, Ilotycin and Sulpha.

The conversation between two doctors' daughters can sometimes sound very weird. Here is a typical telephone conversation:

"Hi, Bets, what's new?"

(Groan). "I didn't sleep a wink last night. Dad had three babies. Population now fifteen million and three. How about your house?"

"Oh, just an acute stomach and some good woman beat up her husband, and Dad had to sew his scalp up — took twenty stitches, too."

Meal time in a doctor's home is always a perfect gem of medical terminology. At breakfast we have bacon and eggs à la gastrectomy Over coffee we hear discussed the pros and cons of a herniotomy or spleenectomy. At dinner we have our steak along with a dissertation on pancreatitis and finish off with apple pie à l'appendicitis.

But the rarest treat of all is to be in a doctor's home at Income Tax time — that time in the calendar year when the coffers of the Department of Internal Revenue are replenished. Then we hear all about coronary thrombosis and cerebral hemorrhages. "I work twenty-four hours a day. The Income Tax Department doesn't care if I drop dead! I'll fool them, that is exactly what I'll do — drop dead."

Heaven help the Minister of Finance if he ever gets into the hands of a surgeon! I shudder to think of what will happen to him.

Being a doctor's daughter can sometimes be most embarrassing. If you are walking down the street, or quietly eating in a restaurant, you can always depend on Father saying, "My what a poor surgical risk that woman will be — must weigh two hundred and fifty pounds. Why do females eat so much? You will have to blast through to get to her appendix!" Or, "See that man with the bald head? I took his stomach out two years ago. Looks good, doesn't he? Never saw so much bleeding. (I am invariably eating a strawberry sundae at this point.) Nice incision, though." And so it goes. I am firmly convinced that when a doctor looks at any human being he sees only a collection of tubes, feed pipes, joints and levers, food and water tanks — in other words, what he sees is not a man at all, but a complicated machine, running very poorly with its carburettor all clogged up. He itches to get at it, to take a monkey wrench and tighten all its joints, or, better still, put a new engine into it.

Lest my readers should never go to see a doctor again, and I, poor creature, be relegated to the poor house, let me assure you they have their fine points. They are patient and true and always unselfish; but that would be material for another essay five times the length of this. Suffice to say, I wouldn't miss for anything the rich and varied experiences of being a doctor's daughter!

MAUREEN J. SABIA,
Ontario

LISTEN, YE SONS OF ALBERTA!

"Hear, ye children, the instruction of a father
and attend to know understanding.
For I give you good doctrine, forsake ye not my law."

Proverbs 4: 1, 2.

Listen, O Sons of Alberta! Kneel at my bedside to hear a historic tale from my dying breath. My story is short, O Sons, but it is a story of triumph. Learn well your lesson by it! Mine is the path you would follow; mine are the deeds you would do. Listen, for I am the Pioneer!

Ten years ere Halley's Comet streaked across the azure sky, my footsteps plodded over a land lost in a wilderness. Fate led me to a gigantic span of rolling hills, open prairies, and lush green forests sheltered in the arms of majestic mountains. That was Alberta!

Mine was the hand that hewed those trees, mine the strength behind the wooden ploughs that tilled the soil, and mine was the backbone of Alberta. But harsh and stern was the wilderness which held her entombed in its iron clasp. Yet strong was my back, young my flesh and hopeful my heart. This was the work for the willing hand: to overcome the stern elements of Nature, to struggle on in the face of defeat, to keep hope strong in the heart, and to work for a better life — for myself and for my children.

Learn well my lesson, you stalwart sons of the pioneers! That fear of the future is a sign of failure; that blazing new horizons with hope and courage is the sign of the Pioneer: this is my lesson!

The ties that bound Alberta as a unit to a young thriving country bound me, the Pioneer, to her roots. In that moment my work began, not for mere existence, but for building blocks, one by one, which were to erect a colossal structure, Alberta! Behold the fruits of this endeavour! Look yonder, Sons! Those cities rising beneath the vast blue sky are tributes to the ambitious hearts; those golden fields of grain are tributes to the unflinching soul. See how the rich oil flows from the redundant soil. See those cattle grazing over the rolling hills. This fertile land is a bread-basket to millions. From its well-filled stores flow the treasures that I have unearthed: wheat, furs, oil, sugar, meat, coal and vegetables. All has been my doing, stupendous and consequential.

Why do I call upon you now? Because . . . because, in flesh, I die. I lived to cleave the land; my task is done. For you and for Alberta, I spent my once exuberant strength. I, a cleaver of the Ages, a Pioneer, must seek my rest.

But, O Sons, the task is not yet done. For fifty years I tutored Alberta; in fifty years I gave her glory. Now your turn has come, your duty to uphold her strength. You must guard the treasures she so bountifully reveals. Do not despoil and leave her barren. Guide her, lead her, uphold her honour, keep Alberta a great province of our great domain – Canada.

And now, this province, this Alberta, whom I have loved, I hand to you on this golden platter. Golden because she bathes in the sun's golden rays, because she gives to you her golden grains, because she is as precious as her weight in gold, and because in fifty golden years as a province, Alberta has triumphed. Take it, Sons of Alberta. This is your heritage – guard it well!

ELSIE KOLODINSKI,
Alberta

THE SEA AT DAWN

In the soft silence of the dawn, the sea
Came rolling 'round the corner of the world.
The giant ocean hit the shore and broke;
The shattered fragments rippling through the sand
Where clams lay buried deep, and broken shells
Were rose and pearl reflections of the dawn.
Above the waves a seagull soared, grey-white
Against the coral sky, and shrieked alone
Throughout the quiet of approaching day.
A piece of driftwood gnarled and old, and rocks
That stood the beatings of the sea, shone bright
With dew and spray. When all things stirred and woke
The miracle of dawn at sea was changed,
And the new wonder of the day was born.

PHYLLIS PARHAM,
Quebec

THE ROBIN

The Robin
hops on the ground
with a breast
of crimson fire
upon the daub brown
of the soil
sings a welcome
to the early wakening
of the earth
in which every soul
has stirred,
breaking
the rest of
the long winter
which melted
into a stream
that goes singing
together with the robin,
harmonizing
each note
a new trend
to recall
the long breath
of summer
for a distance
till
the white sheet
of winter
comes again.

MARY C. SYROID,
Alberta

NEWFOUNDLAND NAME-LORE

Visitors to Newfoundland often wonder at the names of our towns. As early as 1504, there were fishermen from several European countries in St. John's harbour. It was they who gave the names at which the tourists wonder.

St. John's itself was named in 1497 by John Cabot, the discoverer of Newfoundland. Cabot entered St. John's harbour on the feast of St. John the Baptist, June 24, and named it in honour of that saint.

The town of Placentia used to be the French capital of Newfoundland. Placentia was chosen because of its very beautiful surroundings. So beautiful did the French think Placentia that they named it Pleasant Place, which in French is *Plaisance.* This has since been changed to the present form of Placentia.

In 1500, Gasper Corte-Real, the Portuguese explorer who was then Governor of the Azores, heard of John Cabot's voyage of discovery. After getting much information about Cabot's voyage, Corte-Real himself set out to rediscover the new world. Later that year he landed at Cape Bonavista, Cabot's landfall. The cape at that time was unnamed, but Corte-Real gave it the name of Bonavista, a fairly common name in Portugal.

While exploring the coast of Newfoundland, Corte-Real entered Trinity harbour in the early sixteenth century. He climbed the small mountain at the back of the town, and looking out into the harbour he saw three arms of water. Since three-in-one reminded Corte-Real of the Blessed Trinity, he named the harbour Trinity.

Cupids, the first settlement in Newfoundland, founded in 1610 by John Guy of Bristol, was first called Cuper's Cove. Cuper was the Manager or Governor of Guy's colony. Later Cuper's Cove became Cupids, a real improvement over the original name.

Near Cupids is the town of Brigus. Some claim that Brigus was once Brig House. Since there is a Brig House in Yorkshire, England, it may be that Brigus is a corruption of that name. Others say that the name came from the brigs or ships that were often seen in the harbour.

When Sir George Calvert started a colony in Newfoundland, he named his settlement Verulam. Later, when the French took possession of the colony, they changed the name to Ferulam. Ferulam has since been corrupted to Ferryland.

In Conception Bay is the island known as Bell Island. This name comes from the large bell-shaped rock at one end of the iron-isle. Detached from the bell is another rock called The Clapper. Also on Bell Island is the lovely town of Wabana. The name is of Indian origin and means the place where the sun rises.

In the time of the French fishermen, many caribou were seen near the present town of Lawn. The French called the caribou *L'ane* or wild ass. Soon the harbour itself came to be known as *L'ane*. However, when the Breton fishermen came, their broad pronunciation changed *L'ane* to Lawn, and Lawn it has remained ever since.

The French also gave the name of *Audiernne* to one of the harbours. Since then the spelling has changed to suit the pronunciation and *Audiernne* is now Oderin.

Belleoram, a town on the south coast, gets its name from Bellorme, a French adventurer who brought people to Newfoundland to settle.

To the French who named Bay *d'Espoir,* the name meant Bay of Hope, but it has been so changed that now it is both spelled and pronounced Bay Despair.

As you can see, many of Newfoundland's place-names are reminiscent of the days when the European fishermen came every year to our shores to prosecute the fishery. There are several names such as Portugal Cove, Spaniard's Bay, Spanish Room, Port aux Basques, Frenchman's Cove, and Fleur de Lys that thus remind us of the nationalities that once made up the population of Newfoundland.

Even though many of the towns have stories connected with their naming, there are others that no matter how much thinking one does, one cannot explain the reason for their nomenclature. Who could tell why Witless Bay, Come-By-Chance, Seldom Come By, and the Horse Chops received their names? Again, why did some settlers choose a bleak and barren spot on the north of the island and call it Flower's Cove?

LILY SULLIVAN,
Newfoundland

AUTUMN

My heart is in the wild wind
A-blowing over the lea;
With leaves all red and golden
As an autumn melody.

My heart is in the autumn rain
In greying symphony,
And with the ever-swaying waves
Of meadow grass and sea.

My heart is with the wild geese
Winging on their way,
And with the frosted willow trees
Just at the break of day.

My heart has gone a-wand'ring
Through autumn, now grown old,
And whispers of the winter wind
Speak of a coming cold.

MARION GATES,
Nova Scotia

MY DREAM SHIP

Mistress moon is sailing
In the ocean called the sky;
The white clouds are her sailing sheets,
Her compass, but her eye.

The white stars are the swimming fish
Of phosphorescent glow,
And when she swings her lacy net
Only moonbeams show.

The night wind is her captain
Who sets her course full true,
And with her wake, the Milky Way,
She sails away from view.

NATURE'S WORK

The crisp, cool earth awoke refreshed
And bathed her children's faces
In dew-drops, clear as crystal rain,
And dressed them all in laces.

With yellow curls the daisy shone;
The rose wore green and pink;
The morning-glories opened wide
And begged to have a drink.

She swept the sky and made it blue,
And hung a cloud to dry;
And then she made a wispy wind
To blow across the sky.

While yet I slept, Dame Nature worked
To make my morning bright;
Since she has shown me what to do,
I'll set MY house aright.

Marion Gates, Nova Scotia

THE LEGEND OF THE THUNDERBIRD

Many moons ago there was a tribe of Indians that lived on the coast of British Columbia. This tribe was blessed by the gods in numerous ways. In the forest there were deer and bear. Berries grew in abundance on the mountain slopes. Fishing was good. Indeed, they had everything they could wish for except a name. For this reason they were not recognized as a great tribe. Farther back than the oldest of the tribe could remember, the proud son of a great chief had disobeyed his father. He was disowned, and so with a small band of followers, he started his own tribe. Henceforth the tribe was nameless. As soon as a name was thought of, news came of another tribe which already bore that name. The nameless tribe had its pride, too. It would not be called the Weasel Tribe, for instance! That was not their only worry. There was rumour that the God of the Sea was angry at them. Every third day great waves rolled high upon the beach. They were as deep as the tallest brave was tall, and came above the highest tide marker. Many children, and even warriors, were carried away, and never seen again. Were the gods angry? Of course – how else could the people explain it?

One of the people lost to the waves was Brown Dove. Then Running Wolf, her husband, had been taken, trying to save her.

These were the parents of Lame Bear, so called because he was injured in a fight with a bear. He lived with his grandmother. They were a familiar sight in the village, an old woman and a lame boy, hobbling along the paths in search of food. Lame Bear was determined to avenge his father's death, though it meant a fight with the gods.

One day he climbed into his canoe. In the distance he could see the headland. From this direction the waves had come. It was easy in the cool morning, paddling quickly and smoothly, but as the sun rose higher and higher, his strokes were slower and slower. He decided to land, but because of his lame leg, he could not walk easily, so as soon as it grew cooler, he returned to the sea in his canoe. The water was calm now, but in one day and two nights more, the waves would start again. Darkness came on him quickly. Tired, hungry, and thirsty, he landed and sprawled on the beach. Soon he was fast asleep.

Next morning he awoke, and drank thirstily from a nearby spring. Then he paddled on. The point in the distance was growing larger, and he could make out an area of destruction. Evidently the waves came much higher here. He headed out to sea because he was going around the point. He hastened his paddling for the second night was descending upon him. Then when he was near the middle of the high cliff-like piece of land, he headed inward. Though it would be hard on his lame leg, he decided to walk across. Then he wouldn't be taking the chance of being caught in the waves.

He pulled his canoe high on the beach, and stared at the stark desolation. He limped higher on the beach, looking at the fallen trees and rotting debris in astonishment. Only a god himself could do such damage.

He climbed on, resting often, and making little headway. Finally he reached timberland. On and on he travelled. Then he reached the crest of the hill. His eyes widened in amazement. Here was even more damage than what he had just left! He ventured down farther, then sat down, well above the high tide mark, and waited. After a short while, a great shadow fell on the land, and Lame Bear heard a piercing scream. Looking up, he saw a large bird—surely the largest bird he had ever seen! Down, down, down it glided, and at last it landed. Lame Bear watched unbelievingly, as the great bird settled its wings.

Then the bird spoke!

"Do not be afraid," it said.

"Who are you?" cried Lame Bear, fearfully.

"I am called the Thunder Bird," it replied. "I am the Maker of

Storms. This is my sacred shrine. Every day I sacrifice a whale here."

It pointed its great wing, and for the first time Lame Bear saw bones bleaching on the sand. Then he understood. This was what made the waves, and it took them two days to get to the Indian Village.

The bird spoke again. "Where do you live?"

Lame Bear told it. Then he made a timid suggestion.

"Great bird, would you come to our village and be our god?"

After the bird thought for a moment, it agreed. Lame Bear was happy until he remembered his father. He had sworn to avenge his death. But Lame Bear had grown to like this huge flying creature, and what chance had he against it?

He spoke again. "Bird, the waves made by you have carried off many of our people, among them my father and mother. I have sworn by the sun, moon and stars that I will avenge their deaths."

"Oh, them?" said the bird. "I have them on my island. Climb aboard, and we will go to see them."

The bird spread out its wings, and Lame Bear awkwardly clambered upon its back. There, exhausted by the bewildering happenings, he fell asleep on his strange feathery bed.

He awoke with a start—they had landed. Stiffly he crawled down, and stretched his cramped limbs. Ahead of him was a small, crude hut. The bird screamed loudly, and out of the hut came Lame Bear's mother, his father, and the other people of the village! His heart filled with joyous surprise. His father told him of good treatment and much food, and the kindness of the Thunder Bird.

"He has promised to come back and be our tribe totem!" said Lame Bear excitedly.

"Come!" cried the bird. "All of you climb aboard."

So up they got, and quickly they sped over the blue waters. Soon they saw their familiar village far below. Down they flew, and landed on the beach. The braves who had gathered there retreated fearfully. Imagine a great bird carrying those who were believed dead! But the chieftain advanced and said, "Let us have a council meeting, brothers."

A meeting was called. Old and young alike attended, and Lame Bear was called upon to tell his story. The Thunder Bird was taken into the tribe, and promised to protect the village for ever more.

And so it was. The carvings of the great bird can yet be seen on the totems of the Tribe of the Thunder Bird.

GAIL ANN KENDALL,
British Columbia

MY WATERFALL

I love to watch my waterfall
A-tumbling down the rocks;
So fair a sight, and real to me,
I think he sometimes talks.

"O ho!" he says, "I know you now,
I've oftimes seen you here;
I recognize your long canoe,
You've been here many a year."

Then answer I, "You're right, my friend,
I often come this way;
I'm so enchanted by your dash,
That now I'm here to stay."

"Hurrah!" cries he, and dances more,
"We shall not part, no, never."
So now I live close by my friend,
And will stay here for ever.

ABBOTT CONWAY, JR.,
Ontario

MAI

L'hirondelle au zéphyr a construit sa tourelle
Et l'écureuil s'enivre à la fraîcheur du thym;
De jeunes fiancés vont sur la passerelle,
Poursuivent dans le buis leur amour clandestin.
C'est le temps de la vie et de la pastourelle.

C'est mai.

La jeunesse bouillonne en un élan de sève;
Tout l'homme en perspective et le clair idéal
Attirent ces guerriers tel un philtre de glaive.
La lutte musulmane et les fluides du Graal
Hantent ces nouveaux preux. C'est un éclat de rêve.

C'est mai.

Le ruisseau déblayé gazouille à la verdure
Des églogues d'espoir. La cigale d'un jour
Se gave au sein des fleurs. Ah! C'est loin, la froidure!
Chaque être, chaque coin trouve son troubadour.
Mon coeur seul est captif, sous le joug d'un lémure.

C'est mai.

Je veux m'épanouir sous de fraîches poussées.
Place . . . Va-t-en lutin! . . . Magiques odyssées . . . !

C'est mai.

ROGER EBACHER,
Québec

NOVEMBER

He sat there between heaven and earth on a thick mat of dead leaves that crackled with his every movement, watching the horizon through narrowed eyes, as the lead grey of the sky reluctantly gave way to a stormy navy blue. It would snow soon. The first November flakes would dust over the frozen ground like a lacy tablecloth and change the drabness to delicacy. It had happened last year, he remembered, and the year before that, and all the years he'd lived here and been happy just being close to the earth.

He knew all the trees intimately. The gnarled and misshapen oaks told him about the years before he came there: the hard years of hurtling winds that deformed their limbs and made tough their bark; the years of rest and soft rains; the golden years when the warm sun filtered through their leaves and made little patches of light on the green grass; the autumn years when they glowed red in a way that was beautiful. There they were now, sooty and humble in November, beside the young trees that pressed eagerly into the wind the way young things do.

He remembered the wind in the years behind him, the way it ruffled his hair and smote him on the face, the way it stirred up the rain and whistled shrilly around the corners of the old log house where he was born. He had always lived in the wind and responded to its shifting moods like a sensitive child.

He shoved his hands into the rough warmth of his jacket pockets and moved restlessly on the pile of leaves. Stiff blades of grass at his feet shivered at a sudden gust, and he shivered too. He used to hear music in the wind, but now it made him cold.

FRAN WILSON,
Ontario

NIGHT AND THE VELDT

With a sudden rush of darkness the veldt
Is clothed in a black mantle, full of sound.
From the dark comes a roar which shakes the ground,
And when it stops a deathly quiet is felt.
Springbok twitch and jerk, for sudden death
Lurks near at hand, when with a scream and growl
A zebra, young and fat, falls dead. A howl
From a jackal, waits for the beast's last breath.
And when the king of beasts is full, the veldt
Scavengers gather to the kill to snap
And tear with claw and tooth as each is dealt
His share of flesh and bone, while vultures flap
From the air, to gorge themselves full, a belt
Of black round the beasts and dawn on their backs.

JERRY ZUK,
Manitoba

A STORM

When the sky turns dark
And clouds lie low,
When thunder bellows
And great winds blow—
A storm is brewing.
When lightning flashes
In streaks so bold,
And when the air
Turns damp and cold—
A storm is brewing.

When the wind is strong
And it blows from the north,
When the limbs of trees
Rock back and forth,
When small birds soar
Overhead in the sky,
Searching for shelter
As the winds blow high –
A storm is brewing.

KAROL KATZ,
Quebec

SONNET

Though summer, like a candle, slowly wanes,
And wavering, sinking, gently ebbs away,
Before it dies in wind and winter rains
One last bright surge flares up – an autumn day.
Memory of the summers that are fled
And promise of the summers yet to be,
Suffused with molten gold and flaming red,
Blaze forth like fiery brands from every tree.
The radiance of the maples, crimson bright,
Is warm as June, though summer days are done;
The mountains, all afire with vivid light,
Are kindled by the slowly setting sun.
The glory fades at last as autumn flies,
And flickering, swiftly as a flame, it dies.

EILEEN MONK,
British Columbia

DOUBLE DOUBLE

Come in, sir. Sit down. Again I must apologize for my humble furnishings . . . ah, but will you not join me in a little nightcap? One of my few remaining vices, sir, but one which I have come to enjoy, and yes, to need. A nightcap lightens the soul and fills the head with the turbulent confusion of dreams.

Dreams. Sir, you have often questioned me concerning my professed bachelorhood, why I have never married. To-night, the other two principals in my unhappy life enjoying the rewards of their earthly lives, as well they may, I have decided to enlighten you.

I am not a bachelor, sir; I am a widower. No, do not offer your sympathy, for my wife has been dead for so many years that she remains but a dim memory, conjured up at will to fill my breast with tenderness or, upon longer thought, loathing. You are shocked that I speak thus of my dead wife? Your shock now, sir, can not compare with the shock I sustained at the finding of a certain letter . . . but allow me to start at the beginning of my sordid tale.

I met my wife forty years ago, sir, exactly forty years ago to-day. We were quite properly introduced by a mutual friend, and before long our reciprocal admiration and respect turned to love. Although I was but a struggling young lawyer, she consented to be my wife, and three months after our initial meeting, we became man and wife.

My wife was beautiful, sir, a frail, exquisite rose imprisoned in a world of pumpkins! Although small and frail physically, her mind and will were indomitable. This trait I greatly admired, for I myself am of a dogged character.

She was a good wife, sir; no man could ask more, and I loved her. Sir! I loved my wife more than life itself! I would have gladly endured the most agonizing tortures of hell's deepest pit in her defense! But she betrayed me.

It was but seven months after our marriage when I found the

letter. I came upon it while rummaging in my wife's desk for a stamp. Although I destroyed it, I memorized it, for had I ever forgotten it, I might have swayed from my purpose. It was a short note, sir, but the reading of those few words shattered my faith in woman!

I can remember it verbatim:

Dearest Anne:

I cannot express to you my joy upon receiving your letter, and having you confirm our love. I had despaired of seeing you again, but now I am asking you to meet me by the water fountain in the municipal park at eight-fifteen tomorrow evening. Do not fail me. I cannot come to you.

With all my love,

Stephen Lester.

I fully intended to follow my wife the following night, and to surprise her with her lover; but I was in such distress that by the time the hour of the meeting had arrived, I had drunk myself into a stupor. Upon awakening and finding the appointed hour come and gone, I contented myself with meditating on my future actions.

I dared not forget the incident, for I did not know to what point their relationship had progressed. Certain small incidents, however, came to my mind and convinced me of the length of their outrageous affair. For instance, a few weeks after our marriage, my wife began taking solitary walks, claiming that she loved the outdoors. Finding the autumn weather extremely uncomfortable myself, I did not accompany her. If she had been seeing this Stephen Lester at that time, then she must have been unfaithful during almost all of our short marriage! I was appalled.

Now, however, I began to appreciate the guarded remarks of our friends—the subtle remarks questioning my wife's fidelity. They knew! She had made me seem ridiculous in my ignorance! She had shamed me by shaming herself, and my pride could not allow that. She had to be punished.

To wreak vengeance on her physically was out of the question. Her frail body would submit and die before she would be able to suffer. Therefore I had to prey on her mind, her dominant, unyielding mind. It would resist and she would fight back with every weapon at her disposal, until finally the unceasing pressure would cause her to have a mental collapse. Yes, that was the best way.

But how was I to accomplish this? The first glimmerings of an idea came upon me the following day when I read in the morning newspaper of a series of mysterious burglaries. Once started, the whole scheme unfolded itself to me detail by detail. The entire plot hinged on one possibility, that Stephen Lester was listed in the telephone directory.

He was! He was an architect. I telephoned him, explaining that he had been recommended to me by one of my clients, and asking him if he would call on me at my residence, as I was planning a remodelling of my house. He agreed, and the date was set.

A week before Lester's visit, I contracted an annoying cold. This fitted in with my plans perfectly. On the pretext that I did not wish her to be exposed to my illness, I quitted my wife's room in favour of the spare bedroom.

For several nights in succession prior to Mr. Lester's visit, I prowled the immediate neighbourhood, easing myself into houses and burglarizing them. I took nothing of extreme value and was always careful to dispose of my booty in the river. The neighbours themselves carried out the next part of my plan.

I returned home one evening to find Mrs. MacMillan, a crotchety old widow in whose home I had done a rather good job of ransacking, talking to my wife. Upon my entering, she hurriedly took her leave, for we were not the best of friends. My wife explained that Mrs. MacMillan was the fourth person who had called that day, and that the subject of all four had been the series of mysterious burglaries in the vicinity.

Claiming that it was necessary for me to go away on business for a few days, I urged my wife to keep a revolver in her bedroom and to use it on anyone or anything who entered the house uninvited.

The following day, again warning her, I left. I did not, of course, leave the city. Instead I took up residence in a nearby hotel, and on the night of Stephen Lester's visit to my home, crawled stealthily through one of the ground-floor windows. (I had become extremely adept at this during my previous escapades.)

Lester arrived at the predetermined time and I met him at the door before he was able to ring the bell. The absence of lights I attributed to a power failure. Providing him with a flashlight, I bade him enter the library. With those words I showed him the door of my wife's bedroom.

I had just reached the window through which I intended to make my escape when the loud report of a gun echoed through the silent house. I knew what had happened. I ran.

I returned home the following day to find my wife in hysterics. The police inspector who was present explained that she had shot and killed a burglar who had evidently been known to her.

I complied with the usual police formalities, and then carefully noted my wife's condition. She was much distressed, but I knew that she would recover from the shock. More had to be done!

She now began receiving anonymous telephone calls and unsigned letters, all accusing her of murder. They kept up for days, weeks, even months. Every day came a reminder of that horrible night. We notified the police, of course, but they were able to reveal nothing. I had been most careful.

By the end of four months, the strain was plainly telling on her. Her hand shook when she held a cup. Circles appeared under her eyes. Her usually even temperament was replaced by an irritable one. She often burst into tears.

Then, one day, she did not return from a walk. I was about to go looking for her when the police telephoned me. My wife had been crossing a busy intersection and had suddenly stopped in the middle of the street. Then she had turned, screaming like a demon, to face an oncoming automobile. . . .

After attending my wife's funeral, I began to live more and more by myself. My acquaintances thought that I was mourning over my bereavement, and trying to forget. If that were the reason for my retirement, sir, I did not succeed. I began to dream. I dreamed that the letter I found was yellow with age, and that there was no municipal park in the city in which I lived. They were horrible dreams!

That was many years ago, sir, but I have been plagued by dreams ever since. They do not come as often now, but when they do, they are even more horrible than the first ones. I have even dreamed that this cosy room is a cell in a mental hospital, and that you are not my friend, but a psychiatrist. But, of course, that is ridiculous, isn't it?

RONALD VINCE,
Ontario

THE MOUNTAIN GOAT

Snow white he stands against the mountain wall,
The hills, the valleys, he surveys them all,
And defies the mountain to make him fall.

Standing there he sees an eaglet try to fly,
And listens to the echo of a cougar's cry,
Who also defies the world to make him die.

RYAN GILLIS,
Alberta

THE TIGER

Up the long, yellow, summer afternoon
With jungle stride
A tiger crept, whiter than any moon,
And fiercer than the glory of the sun.
All through the humid, heatsick, cloudy day
His quickening feet
Padded the great gray cloud-floor of the sky,
And, hurrying with an ever faster beat,
By evening shone across a gulf of storm
Like fourfold portents of a coming doom. . . .

SNOWFLAKES

Fall, snowflakes, fall;
Fall from the graying vault of the dead and ashen sky,
Fall from the lands of the jewel-dusted constellations
Into the hands of many nations,
Fall from the lap of the winter wind
Onto the waiting world behind
Fall from the curdled, fleecy clouds on high,
And with ermine and pearl and silver cover all.

Fly from the hoary heavens, fly,
Fly from the bosom of infinite space,
From the haunts of the pointed prismic stars,
Where the suns and the moons cast molten spars
Of light,
Golden and white;
Fly from the regions of God's own face,
Fly from the arch of the wind-blown sky.

EDWARD LACEY, Ontario

Author's Note: I wish to dissociate my present self from these two poems as they represent an emotional excrescence of my adolescence of which I am now neither proud nor ashamed, but which I consider neither to be good poetry, nor to give promise of better, unless in the very narrow vein of the nature lyric. — E.L.

MOOD

I was not hungry
Till I ate, nor sad until
I had wept a while.

GYPSY DANCE

Last night . . . the firelight,
Quick brown feet and tambourines;
Today . . . grey ashes.

REVISITED

The three of us sat on a wooden fence . . .
A criss-cross fence of weather-silvered logs . . .
And felt the sunshine through our cotton shirts.
Before us, autumn fields were bright with wheat
That rippled in the wind. The russet trees
Made whispering sounds. Because the sky was blue
And we were young, and countless azure days
Lay in the years ahead . . . we sang out loud.
We sang off-key, no doubt; when we forgot
The words, we hummed, contentedly. The sky
Was blue that day! When we had sung each song
Twice through, we cut long branches from a bush . . .
Green branches, slender, supple in our hands,
And swished them through the drowsy autumn air.
They made a whistling noise, keen and thin,
That sounded more like winter . . . out of tune
With slow warm breeze and ripened fields and trees
That drooped their boughs, too heavy with bright fruit.
We threw the sticks away and watched them make
Slim arcs against the sky. A crow wheeled lazily.

We leaned against each other, watching it,
For we were young and every tiny thing
Was beautiful: an apple's ruby glow
Between the leaves, a bird-song, thin and sweet,
A white cloud in the sky. Now two of us
Are gone. I went back yesterday, alone.
The fence was there, but strangely gaunt and great:
The bones of some dead dinosaur, half-seen
Through grey, damp fog. The trees were bare and black
And lonely. Shreds of mist clung clammily
To their thin hands, and swirled uncertainly
Like strange and half-forgotten dreams. . . .

INCONGRUITY

Smells of ink and chalk,
And rules for binomials,
When the sky is blue!

DEPARTURE

Strangers will trample
Beneath these sun-filled birch trees
Where my dreams are spun.

MICHELE LANDSBERG,
Ontario

THE VOICE

Amua, the blue one, crouched in his kraal, brooding over his misfortune. The Lord, his Lord, had failed him again. Wah! What good were spells and cures and dances? Why, a sign would not turn these goats of people he was amongst. Yet the dream he had had was not one to be ignored. Preaching three all-powerful spirits in one who came to save the world; these were the things it said.

"Go forth unto all tribes," it had told him, "teach my people the way of the Lord." Ah, such was the glory in the dream it would take him many months to describe it. He had been told to preach for the Lord, and Wangdo, his father, could not have preached better than himself. He danced two dances each day for all to see, and he had put many spells on the great green water-killer that preys on the unwary. His mother, greatest witch of the south veldt, had never treated a lion-wound so that it healed. All this, and more, had he done in preaching, and still they would not believe in the Lord who had sent him.

"Amua, the blue one, are you within?" called a voice just outside the entrance to his kraal.

"I am, what do you desire?" answered the witch-doctor moodily.

"Tongay Madu, chief of the Todus, wishes to have parley with you," announced the voice.

"He may do so at any time," replied Amua. "Does he wish to enter and speak now?"

"Nay, the great chief, though not wishing to offend you, asks that you parley with the council in the circle, when the sun is impaled on the head tree," declared the voice; adding as an afterthought, "He wishes to speak with you concerning your Lord."

Amua grunted his assent; the chief was up to no good. This council parley was certainly being called to get rid of him. The wizard shivered, for he knew well the methods the Todus used to get rid of people. This reminded him to check the time, which he did by comparing the position of the sun in relation to the chief's head-tree; it would be a long time before it was on the tree.

Thinking of the tree made Amua remember certain other methods and customs of the Todus, and he shivered again. But what was he crouched here for? He would work a spell, his last spell. It would be a spell that no witch doctor could ever do again, and, with this thought, he began to prepare his powders and charms.

The drums were sounding low when Amua stepped from his kraal into the council-circle. His Lord was with him, he knew, for he had dreamed again.

"The Lord is with you always," it had said, "and He is thy shield and thy strength."

Ah, at least he had protection! His God would not desert him. Having thought this out, he lifted his head high and entered the circle.

Tongay Madu advanced, wearing besides his full war regalia, a heavy frown. Disregarding the customary greetings, he spoke at once.

"Amua, son of Wangdo, the south veldt wizard, though we respect your power in spells, we ask you and your God to leave us. Spells you have given us and cures and charms, yet gods we want not. If your God is less powerful than our thunder-god, what would become of us if we worshipped both? Our thunder-god would destroy your Lord and us. You teach us hard things to obey one god and obey no other god, and we do not wish to listen. We ask you to leave."

The wizard well knew that he had lost the chance to argue. Exile was worse than death for him, a spellmaker. He was about to make a vain effort to speak when an elder arose and stepped forward.

"Blue one," said he very slowly, "be not angry and bring a spell upon us. We shall give you a chance to prove your Lord. If he speaks with thunder louder than our god, and speaks in a voice that causes the trees to shake, we shall accept him willingly. I warn you, though, if you say he comes and he does not, spellmaker though you are, I fear for your head." Having said this, the elder went to his place and squatted down.

Here was a chance that only his Lord could have given him; it was a test! What could he say? Say his Lord could not thunder, and be banished, or say that he could, and maybe lose his head? He turned to his Lord for help, imploring to be given guidance. Suddenly a little voice within him began to speak. He could only understand a phrase of it, but that was enough.

"And ye shall hear the voice of the Lord." Amua nodded and spoke to the council.

"As you asked it, my Lord will show you – he shall speak." As an afterthought he brashly added, "Aye, he shall also speak of destruction to those who do not turn to Him."

The council, indeed the whole tribe, stared at him unbelievingly. Such a thing was blasphemy! The thunder-god would surely strike him down. Even as they thought, a low rumbling noise could be heard in the distance. The rumble increased to a roar, the roar to thunder. Yet, above the noise a voice could be heard.

"Attention, white settlers! The eastern and western alliances are at war. Every person is needed urgently. Return to civilization immediately."

The voice faded out, the thunder softened. In the light of the sinking sun, Amua caught a glimpse of what looked like a great white bird. All he could really remember was the voice, and all he could say was, "The voice of the Lord, it was the voice of the Lord."

M. J. TAMPLIN,
Ontario

NIGHT

Dusk is a blue-purple iris,
Slipping from its greengold stem
Into cool water, letting fall and colouring the sky
With a pale, pale stole of night, as thin as gauze.

Then the sun's warm finger-tips slip over the cliff,
And the earth, shivering,
Draws the thick robe of night closer round her still,
And lights the night-light of the moon.

But the ghost-like lights of the little stars
Peer round the corners of the sky;
And the earth, frightened, huddles under her cloak
And fumbles for the golden ball of life

Which is the sun. The hillocks
Hump themselves in fear, and the birches
Cling to one another's hands and tremble.
Then the first brazen notes of a young cock's crow

Riddle holes in the world, and it awakes,
Awakes to see grey trees lying in
The pink and pearly arms of the sky.
And then the petals of the day unfold, and the sun is up.

CYNTHIA CREIGHTON,
Ontario

DAYDREAMING

The springboc, with its light step, the swift meadow lark on the wing, the antelope with its far-carrying leap, all are swift and able to reach afar with ease; but I, a human being, possess the greatest and easiest method of travel. I possess the wings of daydreaming. At any time, any place, I can mount my golden steed of imagination and be carried through forests of adventure and excitement, peace and contentment, to the farthest reaches of the universe. Worlds I alone can possess await me, to serve me, with only a thought to bring me to rein.

As does everyone who makes use of this universal means of answering one's wishes, I dream of the things I most want to do or the things I would like to have. My thoughts range from north to south, from China to Mexico or to nowhere in particular. Or, as after reading a science fiction book, to places as yet, and probably always, unheard of. I meet new and interesting people and things. I can accomplish the impossible and improbable, own anything, anywhere, with naught to stop me except in the case of a glowering teacher who thinks I should answer the question I have just been asked for the third time. However, after the subsequent rebuffing and a tactical elapse of attentive time I return to the thought at hand.

Throughout the world scenes similar to these are enacted. Men and women, young or old, while enjoying a moment's relaxation, and with nothing better to do, escape the humdrum of life that wealth brings, or the want of poverty or the everyday happenings by making use of their mind's artificial senses of sight, etc., called imagination. Some thumb through pages of past experiences, long stored away in vast vaults of memory, while others think of things to come or things they wish would come. So I know that when I daydream it does not necessarily mean that I have a lazy mind, but that by daydreaming I may realize a secret ambition and thus spur myself on to getting my wants and thus lead a full and proper life. Other men have had daydreams and found a way to make them come true. Marco Polo, Columbus, Pasteur, the Spaniards who conquered Mexico, all had daydreams and realized them. On the other hand, a tyrant named Hitler had a daydream of power. This kind of daydream, true, can be destructive, but had he gone about it with love for his people and diplomacy, instead of V-2 rockets and Messerschmitts, Hitler might have established a firm and happy nation.

Thus, daydreaming is an international exit from the facts and may be a mere fancy or a dream which in time may come true. When I dream, however, I do not dream of power as Hitler or the rulers of Japan did, but of mere fancies. After all, why should I dream of power? I control the universe and its inhabitants with my powers of imagination. Can I not cause Robin Hood to leap through my mind's Sherwood Forest or imagine driving a new Cadillac through Florida? Yes, these things and many more I can bring about in my mind as I possess the greatest Alladin's Lamp of all. I possess the wings of imagination.

LA ROY MARSDEN,
Alberta

ALONE

Far from home, in a foreign land, I was alone.

I could not speak their language, nor could they understand mine. I was isolated in the midst of a score of strange faces.

The faces had pinched, hungry looks. The eyes were glazed and sullen. The lips were parted and the yellow fangs of teeth gave the faces a bestial appearance.

Night was drawing near and this primeval tract of jungle was no place to be trapped in the night, alone. I had been travelling since before day-break hoping to reach the hunting preserve where my friend, John Ashley, worked. They had told me I was a fool to travel in the jungle alone, but my guide was sick, my vacation was nearly over, and my determination to see my schoolmate once more was unshaken.

Now I began to regret my impetuosity. Old tales of head-hunting, and voodoo, and vanishing hunters came back to haunt me. Hurriedly, I approached the headman's hut. The sooner I could check my bearings and press on towards Ashley's lodge, the better.

These natives could not speak my tongue but at least if I was on the right trail they would know John's name. The headman's face made me shiver. The cruelty of the untamed beast lurked in his eyes. Civilization was far away and little heeded in these jungle retreats. Indeed John had told me in his letter that often months went by without his seeing a friendly face.

The thought of John's blunt, English face soothed me and I accosted the old chief boldly enough.

"Tuan Ashley," I cried and waved my arm questioningly towards the bushes. The old man hesitated, then suddenly he leered and beckoned me to follow him into his hut. Sheer terror gripped me but somehow I followed him. I was desperate now for the sight of a friendly face in the midst of these black leering natives. I think I would have followed Satan into the infernal darkness. My guide stopped and stepped aside. For the briefest second I felt I was going to die. Then I knew for certain that I was.

I had found my friendly face at last but the great strong body that had carried John Ashley so far was not attached to it any more.

ROBERT AMARON,
Quebec

FARM TO THE FINISH

The greatest fight I ever saw was Joe's struggle to be a successful farmer. His one aim in life was just that. He was in there slugging away every minute striving for success on his one hundred and seven acres. Poor Joe was always two blows behind. There were the beetles, the grasshoppers, and the caterpillars to contend with. There was also a drought in spring, a hailstorm in summer, and an early frost in the fall. But the invaders that worried him most came from the nearby city of Edmonton. They were pushing their housing developments farther and farther afield, and pretty soon they began to edge into Joe's farm.

Joe was forced to sell some of his land here and some of it there. He brought home the money and put it in a bag. His wife Alfreda would put the money in the bank from time to time. The smaller the farm got the harder Joe and his kids struggled to make a go on what was left. The city grew, the farm shrank, and Joe grumbled.

Once in a while Joe would sit down in the evening and think of all the fun they used to have when the farm was his father's and he and his brothers and sisters were small children. When the summer sun was at high noon and the water was warm they'd go for a swim in the creek that now already belonged to the city of Edmonton. In the fall he'd enjoyed himself by going hunting, and in the winter, by trapping weasels and muskrats. Another memory came back to him. It was of the time when he was fifteen, when he and his father had spent days in the summer planting trees around the farm to prevent wind erosion. He'd always loved to see them grow. Now the trees were being chopped down and piled, ready to be burned. It was a shame the way they did things. But that's the way it was.

Finally, the last of the cultivated fields went to the city folks. "That does it!" growled Joe. "The farm's gone. All we got left in the world is the house, the barn, the old garage with the new Cadillac in it, and—hey, Alfreda, did you put away that last $97,000? Yeh, let's see—and $826,299.71 in the bank."

EDWARD WENSEL,
Alberta

THE SNOWFLAKE

Tiny elf, who fashioned you?
Who wove your purest lace?
Who made your perfect features?
Who blessed you with such grace?

Are you a tear some angel shed,
Kissed by the crystal frost?
Are you the dainty garment
Some fleeing fairy lost?

Or can you be a message,
Sent down from up above,
To remind us of our Maker?
Do you bring with you His love?

Tiny snowflake swirling;
Dancing from the sky;
I can only wonder,
As you glide gaily by.

Maria Adams,
New Brunswick

DEW-DROPS

The little angel strummed a chord
Upon her harp of gold
The strings sent forth the harmony
Of an anthem worn and old.

The strings played sweetest harmony
Softly, tremblingly, true:
But the angel was weary of soft sweet sounds
And her tears fell as heavenly dew.

She laid down the golden harp
And wept on her fluffy white cloud,
For just the sound of an earth-bird's song,
Discordant, clear and loud.

Frances Wagstaffe,
Ontario

SILENCE SONGS

Mist kisses,
Glistening mouth-marks
On the hilltop;
Mist hair
Clinging damply to the forehead of the earth —
Cloud-infants, young and sheer as spider's spinnings;
Mist, mist,
Mist-kissed mother earth.

White dawn
Creeps silently over the horizon,
Revealing the woods draped in vapour,
Still and sacred as a praying nun.

The sun
Bounds riotously into the sky,
The wood shakes off her ritual garments,
And dances, like a pagan in the wind.

Shirley Wright,
British Columbia

THE MOUTH ORGAN

Mr. Crawson was well-known in Thistletown. He had served in the Merchant Marine during the World War, and now, an old man, retired with a small confectionery and toy shop at the corner of May and Hampden Streets. His daughter was married and moved to the city, so that the old man was all alone—but not quite, for he had his little guests. He was a favourite with the boys of the neighbourhood, who flocked to his shop every day, and were received with hearty generosity. Often he would 'spin yarns', as he called it, of his adventures on the high seas, and they would listen with open mouths and burning eyes. These were the happiest moments of the old man's life.

One day, there came a boy into the store, whom Mr. Crawson had never seen before. He had light blue eyes that distinctly peeped out through his long, red hair.

"Ahoy, there, young man!" Mr. Crawson greeted him. "And what can I do for you this fine morning?"

"H'lo," replied the boy, in a thin, shrill voice, and pointing to the window asked, "That small mouth organ, may I see it?"

"Why, certainly, my lad," said Papa Crawson, and showed him the toy with a fatherly understanding smile.

The boy reached for it eagerly, and caressed its shiny, gilted sides with small and rather dirty hands.

"Can you play one?" asked Mr. Crawson. The boy shook his head silently.

"Then I'll teach you," said Papa Crawson, and took a much larger mouth organ out of his pocket, explaining, "This is my priceless possession. She was a blessing to me during the hard days in the Atlantic. Whenever I became gloomy, I just played a lively tune, and was on top of the world again. D'ye know this one?" he asked suddenly, and began to play a familiar sea chant on the ancient mouth organ.

The boy was delighted. "Were you really a sailor?" he asked, when the old man had finished playing.

"Indeed I was," replied the other most emphatically, and seeing the cue, he lighted his pipe and began.

"Seeing that you're new around here, perhaps you didn't hear any of my yarns." He seemed to be closely examining his pipe, as though trying to find some hidden, secret story, and then, suddenly, he pointed it straight at the blank face of the boy whose head just protruded above the counter, and fired, "Did you ever hear of the Solomon Islands?"

It was a masterful beginning. He saw the puzzled expression of the boy, and smiled with satisfaction.

"I see that you're no professor of geography. Wait here a minute, I'll go and get a map," – and he rushed off, leaving the boy alone in the store to stare after him.

"Now where could that map be," he asked himself, opening one drawer after another. "I have him under my spell. There are so many interesting things I could tell him, so many valuable lessons I could teach him. He looks like a fine little fellow. Oh, here it is!"

He grabbed the map with trembling hands, and rushed off, full of expectations. As he burst into the store room, his eager face changed to an expression of mingled surprise, bewilderment and pain. Suddenly, he felt all alone in the world, and his eyes glistened. The small mouth organ and the boy were gone.

YARKO LEVYTSKY,
Ontario

THE CANADIAN FIELD

The sun rose up in the morning,
White frost was on the ground,
The wheat stood up in sheaves of gold,
In the air was nary a sound;
The brown earth crunched with the heavy frost,
The rooster uttered his clarion call,
For this is a field on the countryside,
On a morning in early fall.

Oh, what stories this field could tell,
If nature bid her to;
She told her tale to me all right,
Perhaps she will to you.

On a sunlit morn in springtime,
While crickets chirped their song,
The green things raised their billowy heads,
Mother Nature could do no wrong;
The dew was a web of silver thread,
A field mouse scampered away,
And a robin stood with a gleam in her eye,
As a worm worked out of the clay.

Across this field in summer time,
The wind waltzes with the grass,
And when the sun sets in the west,
A little red fox trots past;
The horse and man sweep the field,
At the start of another day,
And when day turns to night again,
There's an odour of new-mown hay.

In the cold crisp air of a winter day,
When the earth is hidden by snow,
Rabbits whisk merrily over the crust,
As Sol sets it aglow;
A magnificent buck in the cedar stand,
Gazes placidly out at the day,
Where, beneath a blanket of pure crisp snow,
Spring is tucked away.

This field could tell of forefathers,
Working the soil long before,
This field could tell of animal life,
And of nature and her lore;
But the field tells something more to me,
With its beasts, and plants, and sod;
It shows how small are the works of man,
Compared to the works of God.

EDWARD BELL,
New Brunswick

SO YOUNG, SO BRAVE

As she opened the door, Janet was greeted by the warm, rich aroma of pie, hot from the oven. "I'm home, Mom," she called from the wide old hall, removing her coat. Janet stood for a moment, lost in thought, a rather tall, dark girl—pretty, with her dark, softly-waved hair gently outlining her face. Finally, her reverie ended, she entered the kitchen.

"Busy at the office today, dear?" asked Mrs. Masters, as Janet kissed her lightly on the forehead.

"No, Mom; and Mom—I have to hurry. I have a date in an hour." Her mother turned from the stove.

"With Dan?"

"No, Mom," replied Janet. "His name is David—David Simpson," and then shyly, "He's very nice!" The sound of the front door opening interrupted their conversation. John Masters entered, tall and graying.

"Hello, dear, steak for supper?" Janet kissed her father as she left the kitchen.

"Yes, John, steak; and you can sit down, it's ready," said Mrs. Masters. "Janet's going out with some young man she's just met—David Simmons, or something like that. I hope he's nice like Dan."

"I'm sure he will be, Martha," replied her husband, sitting down. "Our daughter's a good, sensible girl."

Later, as both sat reading over their coffee, Janet having gone upstairs to get her coat, the doorbell rang.

"I'll get it, Martha," said her husband. "It will probably be Janet's young man." He opened the door and his face froze.

After an awkward silence, the young man said:

"I'm David Simpson: I'm here for Janet."

"Come in," said Mr. Masters, his voice faltering. At that moment, Janet came quickly down the stairs, then stopped.

"Hello, David," her voice was soft. "Dad, this is David Simpson; David—my father." David held out his hand.

"I'm pleased to meet you, sir." Janet's father hesitated, then shook the outstretched hand.

"We'll have to run, Dad, or we'll miss the beginning of the show," said Janet hurriedly. "Bye – 'bye, Mom."

"Good-bye, sir," said David quietly. Mr. Masters' good-bye was shaky as the two left.

"Martha, you saw him; what shall we do?" His wife's face was pale and drawn and she did not speak.

It was midnight when the car's lights shone in the window as it turned into the driveway. Neither of Janet's parents, who sat stiffly in the living-room, spoke. A few minutes later the door opened.

"Hello, folks," said Janet, entering the room.

"Janet, sit down; your mother and I have something to say to you." Her father's voice was strained and unreal as he spoke.

"It's about David, isn't it?" she replied quietly.

"Oh, Janet," her mother cried out, "How. . . ."

"Just a moment, Martha," interrupted Mr. Masters. "Don't get yourself upset. Now, Janet, this Simpson is no doubt a very nice fellow, but he's not our kind. What would your friends think if they saw you with him? You could hardly expect them to welcome him. And you could never become – well . . . serious. Don't you think. . . ."

Janet broke in, her voice low but firm:

"Dad, listen to me. I like David very much. In time I may love him; now, I don't know. I don't care what colour his skin is. He is a fine man and that is all that is important. If my friends won't accept him, then I don't want them for friends. I am going to continue going out with him, and there's nothing you or anybody else can do to stop me. Now I'm going to bed; I'm very tired. Good-night, Dad; good-night, Mother." As she finished speaking, Janet turned and without looking back, ascended the stairs. John Masters turned to his wife and spoke. Far into the night the steady murmur of conversation continued, broken only by an occasional excited outburst.

The haze of morning was giving way to the rich glow of the rising sun when Janet, dressed for the office, came slowly down the stairs. Despite her efforts to the contrary, her thoughts dwelt on the previous evening's happenings. Entering the kitchen, she was greeted cheerily by her mother.

"Good morning, dear, breakfast's ready." As the three ate, a strained silence enveloped the table.

Finally Janet's father cleared his throat awkwardly and spoke. "Janet, if you are going out with David this evening, why don't you bring him home afterward? Your mother will have some of those special sandwiches of hers made and. . . ." His voice died out slowly. Janet smiled warmly.

"Thanks, Dad, I'd love to. I'm sure you'll like David."

"I'm sure we will, dear," said her mother gently. "I'm very sure we will."

It was dusk. In the living room, John Masters read the evening paper; in the kitchen, his wife, Martha, stood ironing; while upstairs, Janet stood before her mirror applying make-up. The doorbell's shrill ring broke the silence of the house.

"Will you get it, Dad?" called down Janet. Her father rose, paused for a moment, then, squaring his shoulders, walked to the door.

"Good-evening, David," he said, as he opened the door. "Come in and sit down. Janet will be down in a moment." He ushered the young man into the living room. "Cigarette?" he asked.

"Thanks, Mr. Masters," replied the younger man taking one. Both men rose as Janet's mother entered the room.

"Oh, Martha," said her husband, "I'd like you to meet David Simpson. David this is my wife, Martha."

"I'm very glad to meet you, Mrs. Masters."

"How do you do, David. Janet will be . . . oh, here she is now." Janet was smiling as she came into the room.

"Hello, David. Have you met mother?"

"Yes, I have," he replied.

"Well, shall we leave," she said. "I'm all ready." Mr. Masters followed them to the door and opened it.

"Good-night, folks," said Janet. "We'll see you later."

"Have a nice time!" called Mr. Masters as they walked to the car. He reached out and took his wife's trembling brown hand in his. "They will too, Martha. It will be hard, but they are young and youth has great courage." Silently they watched the blonde young man help their daughter into the car, her brown arm resting on his white one. The car was started and soon passed out of sight. Slowly the door closed.

Clive Lytle,
British Columbia

SPEED

Speed is the sight of –
swift cars, trim boats, fleet horses,
silver wings.

Speed is the sound of –
roaring motors, flapping sails, thudding hooves,
screaming jets.

Speed is the smell of –
burnt rubber, salt water, hot horses,
kerosene.

Speed is the feel of –
rushing wind, wet spray, stinging sand,
space.

Judy Earle,
Ontario

FOG

The lights of the tranquil city wink softly in the
Mellow darkness; when slowly from the harbour
Long willowy fingers come twisting and sliding.
The wispy threads grow gigantic, and
Slowly encircle the city in a moist cloak.
Gradually the lights dim and then fade,
All is calm; then under the dusky mantle
Shadowy figures creep stealthily about.

The fog watches the sly and the skulking,
It hides evil hearts and sinister faces,
And grins at their grotesque stories,
But lies mute . . .
Suddenly the moon peers through the gauzy veil,
And slowly, slowly the fog flows from the city;
The fingers withdraw and turn again
To the sea with their secrets.

MARILYN ROBERTSON,
British Columbia

GUESS WHAT?

Since this is the season for aquatic sports like basketball and skiing, I thought I might give you some sound advice on choosing a horse.

There are three main kinds of horses: black, white and brown. The white horse, as anyone knows, is much faster than the black or brown horse. This may be proved by the fact that all of the heroes in Western movies ride white horses. To choose a good horse, you must know its main features. Here I will deal with each feature in a paragraph.

Legs: If you desire the utmost in speed from your horse, I would advise you to buy one with legs. Although the price may be slightly higher it is well worth it. Most horses have four legs and it seems to be a very satisfactory arrangement. There are, however, horses with eight legs, that is, two on the front, two on the back and two on each side. (Each horse has two sides.)

Eyes: If you buy a horse to ride in the country it is best to get one with 18-18 or 20-20 vision. You can have your horse's eyes checked at any good optometrist. Sight is one of the horse's most important senses. If you buy a blind horse he is liable to step in a gopher hole and break his leg (presuming you have the legged variety). Then you will have to shoot him, and carry your saddle to the road to wait for the first stage coach. These days that might be quite a wait. However, you might buy a seeing-eye dog that can speak horse-language.

Body: The body serves two main purposes. One is to hold up the saddle. Although you may not know it, this is a very important function. Have you ever wondered how you would sit on the horse if there were nothing to hold up your saddle? The second and most important function of the body is to keep the front and rear legs apart (again presuming you have a horse with legs). If your horse had not a body to keep its legs apart it would continually be stepping on its own feet and stumbling, which makes a very uncomfortable ride.

Ears: It is necessary for your horse to have ears because a deaf horse cannot hear you whistle and therefore cannot come and kick the door down and drag you out of the burning house like Hank Hawkeye's horse did in 'West of the Pecos'.

Head: The last main part of the horse is its head. It serves as a container for the all important eyes which have been mentioned before. It also serves to hold the ears apart, making it necessary for the horse to have two. You can always tell if a horse has a head by looking between its ears. If the bases of the ears are not touching, the horse has a head. I advise you to purchase a horse immediately because as everyone knows, automobiles are just a passing fancy, and the price of horses is liable to rise anytime.

Some horse lovers will pay as much as three dollars and fifty-nine cents for one horse.

If you follow this advice carefully when choosing your horse you will have a faithful steed which you could ride to Paris, France, if it weren't for the ocean.

GARY EARLE,
Ontario

THE FORSAKEN

Myrtle huddled her awkward body as closely to the grey stone of the Academy as she dared. She did not wish to attract attention — only because she realized the type of attention warranted her.

The rest of the students rushed out through the big doors, gaily chattering about their plans for the long weekend. Myrtle thought how she would spend her holidays . . . going home to a filthy house to hear her brothers and sisters screaming at each other; or to see her mother in a torn and faded workdress wearily scolding her stepfather. He would have received his pay and spent it at one of the many bars. No, the girl with the thin face and roughened hands did not anticipate the coming days.

She thought of school as a refuge from the continuous quarreling and the whining children. Myrtle loved the cool stones of the building itself, and the wide, spacious hallways. But most of all, she considered the quietness of the library a refuge. While devouring one of the precious books she entered into a world all her own — a world where no ugliness or bitterness broke the tranquility.

Abruptly, a high, mocking voice broke her chain of thoughts.

"Oh, it's that little worm from Scullay Square," she shrilled, "Does your pa still spend his pay at Tacey's Bar or has he shifted his trade to Pete's?"

Myrtle's sallow cheeks became deathly white then flared crimson. The speaker was Sheila Vanderbeck, the president of the Student's Council, and the most popular girl in school. Of all the others, Myrtle envied Sheila most. How she longed for her blonde lustrous hair and the lithe, graceful figure! How she craved a little of the worship and attention showered upon the unworthy Sheila! Now, to be humiliated in front of the whole school by her idol was the crowning shame in Myrtle's life. Never again could she face the others or enjoy the peacefulness of the Academy—for now there was no peacefulness. A few short words uttered without thought, a light scornful laugh had shattered the only life the girl from the 'wrong side of the tracks' had left. Rushing blindly through the remaining students, her eyes filled with scalding tears, she stepped into the moving traffic.

She didn't see the on-coming truck, nor did she hear the deafening crash and the hysterical screams. Perhaps it was better like that! A flock of students led by Sheila swarmed into the street and around the crumpled body. Now, for the first time in her lonely life Myrtle was the centre of attention. But she did not care. . . .

KAREN POLEY,
Quebec

AUTUMN'S AGE

What does autumn mean to you?
Northern lights when day is through,
Honking geese in shrouded skies,
Football games and frenzied cries,
Days that sparkle like rich wine,
Flaming maple, green-robed pine,
Crackling leaves on woodland walks,
Flickering flames at fireside talks?

Heavy-headed golden wheat
Shimmering in the hazy heat
Of an Indian summer day?
Scudding clouds above the bay
Where three sailboats smoothly glide
As if caught by restless tide?
Flaming sunsets rich and rare,
Trees with stars caught in their hair?
You're young!

What does autumn mean to you?
Rain, and muddy overshoe,
Storms to cart from out of storage,
Frosty days and luke-warm porridge,
Children's snowsuits, now too small,
Cedar chest, and stale mothball,
Frost to kill the last rose-bud,
Icy rain-storms, puddles, mud?
You're old!

PAT ROBINSON,
Ontario

TOO MUCH TURKEY

The camp fire flickered and died out. The last traces of scarlet were lingering on the western horizon. The trees on the river bank cast long shadows on the water while a coyote in the distance stuck his nose toward the yellow moon and howled. An owl hooted from a nearby clump of trees. Night had fallen and all was still.

I sat, munching a drumstick with my back to the trunk of a cedar tree. A curious jack-rabbit bounced along through the tall grass. His ridiculously long ears stood at attention when he saw me. I tossed the bone at him and watched him bound away. I got up, kicked some dirt on the smouldering fire and crawled into the sleeping bag. My first night in the wild and woolly west coming up. It was too lonely out on the prairie so I had pitched camp by this slow moving river. Trees of all kinds grew near rivers in Texas and formed some tropical forests abounding in wild life and completely untouched by civilization. It was an ideal place for a holiday . . . except for the Indians, for the year was 1863 and the fierce Apaches were still terrorizing the southwest.

I lay awake in the sleeping bag, thinking of the fun I had had the past day. I thought of the troop of wild turkeys I had surprised and of the meal just finished. I remembered the fright I got when I was just about to jump into the river for a swim and nearly mistook an alligator for a half submerged log. A troop of stately deer, trooping to the water just before sunset had provided me with a spectacle which I would never forget. Out on the prairie I had watched a vast herd of shaggy buffalo grazing on the rich buffalo-grass. Through a pair of field glasses I saw a few antelope but on horseback I just couldn't get close to them because of their blinding speed. And now, tired as I was, the vivid pictures of the past day swam before my mind so rapidly that I was not able to get to sleep.

The woods seemed lonely now that the continual chirping of the birds had changed to the eerie hooting of owls. The moon was a pale yellow shade and made the trees cast sinister shadows on the ground. Once I thought I heard padded footsteps. I quickly reached for my gun and carefully loaded it. These footsteps might have meant a cougar or possibly a jaguar—maybe an Apache! The thought struck me like a bullet and left me shaking and shivering. I had heard some pretty bad stories about the Apaches. It must have been hours later before I dropped off to sleep.

I opened my eyes with a start, yet I did not know what had awakened me. I stretched and turned over to get in a more comfortable position. The sight I saw made my blood run cold.

Not five feet away from my bulging eyes was an Apache Indian, on all fours, with a long knife that sparkled in the moonlight. He did not budge, but stared menacingly at me, his bronzed, half naked body slender and glistening with grease. There were streaks of yellow and red warpaint from his small black eyes to his chin. His hair was long and black and the breeze tossed it wildly about. His face was wrinkled and showed a thin, cruel set of lips set tightly together.

I was frozen to the spot, petrified with fear, staring into the eyes of this savage. Sweat started to drip off the end of my nose. Slowly his mouth broke into an evil smile, showing rows of white teeth. He uttered a blood curdling shriek and lunged at me. The knife hovered in the air and descended. I looked at my chest and saw the knife, buried to the hilt.

I woke up shaking and sweating. What a nightmare. In my death throes I had nearly rolled into the river.

Now the forest was green again. The birds were singing, the sky was blue and the sun was shining brilliantly. I was hungry. I lit the fire and dug up a few worms. While waiting for the kettle to boil I cut myself a trouting pole and went down to the river.

Ten minutes later my frying pan boasted two fine red-bellied trout and a strip of juicy bacon. No more turkey for me. It made me dream too much.

DAVID QUINTON,
Newfoundland

THE FLOODS CAME

From tiny rivulets oozing out of the damp and spongy earth, laughing and chattering, to the furrows rushing through the brown fields, to the wood paths, to the creeks dashing and swirling, cutting through crumbling clay banks, to the swollen spreading rivers, so came the flood.

Down river in the village the ice is still out, great masses of white and grey lying motionless now, but waiting. In the general store, the drowsy talk of the old men shifts from an auction sale to the weather and the ice. How soon will it break? A week, two weeks . . . each gives his opinion, then draws deep again of the blue smoke of clay pipes. These are the old men. Once they were young, and gloried in their strength, in their youngness. Now they have nothing, nothing but memories, memories. . . .

Slowly the sacks of flour and cotton dresses and harness fade from view. Sixty years have rolled back. Scattered on the mountain sides are tiny chinked log huts surrounded by a few bare fields. A boy, just beginning to get his growth, watches from a hillside and listens and wonders.

Huge boulders of ice batter and grind in deep agony as they push their way down the swirling whirlpool above the mill, jamming against restraining wooden planks and earthen banks. Swiftly around the river bend glides an uprooted tree, its roots like tentacles grasping at the water as it rolls and rocks on down, overtakes a promontory and twists around in eddying current. Water, swirling, throbbing water, pounding, tearing, uprooting, destroying all that cannot flee. Water, the friendly water, has gone mad. From upland creeks and fields it has hurried, leaping through gullies, cutting new channels, rolling rocks aside, hurrying, hurrying with one purpose—destruction! It twists and heaves, pounding the ice against the dam in sledge hammer blows until its weakened sinews are broken. Then, like a fanatical army it rushes over the tiny village, ripping up picket fences and rose bushes, pouring into kitchens and cellars, rocking, bursting, in a wild orgy of destruction, tearing at the very roots of buildings, at the very roots of life, silencing the bawling cries of cattle and of sheep trapped in barns and on hillocks – greedy in its destruction!

Then, its energy spent, it grows calmer, lapping at the eaves of houses, eddying around windows and doorways. It dies, dropping back into the river bed, its fevered brain rational, once more ready to be the servant of man.

And the boy on the hill and the old man in the sleepy store wonder why it had to be.

BILL LAIDLAW,
Ontario

THE HIDDEN GRAVE

The song of the birds in the little green valley
Echoed in plaintive and mournful refrain
Over the tops of the towering pine trees,
Past the soft rolling breadth of the plain;
Over to a small spot, secluded, alone,
Where whispering poplars and small willows stood,
By trembling grasses and nodding pink roses,
And daisies that sprinkled the heart of the wood.

I strolled through the woods on a bright day in summer,
Through the green woods in this valley of peace,
Quiet and hidden in the depth of the woodland
Beneath a blue sky that was dotted with fleece;
Alone stood I there with the tall trees around me,
'Mid quivering patterns of sunlight and gloom,
When I saw to the side this small spot of beauty,
Encircled with hedges and flowers in bloom.

And there in the heart 'mongst the grass and the branches
Rose a simple white cross crowned with a wreath
Made of blossoms and leaves that long had been wilted
And weepingly drooped on the wording beneath:
"Sweeter she was than the fragrant red roses,
Pure as the lilies that smile with the dawn,
Beautiful as the red cloud of the sunset,
But with the last sunbeam, has faded and gone."

There I stood gazing in sadness and wonder,
Musing the words o'er that cold mound of clay;
Who lies here? Who mourns her? Why the grave in the
forest?
These questions unanswered — I know not today.
But e'er I remember that grave in the valley,
The little white cross and the sad, faded wreath,
The message in memory of some loved one lost,
That once had been written in sorrow beneath.

When the song of the birds in the little green valley
Echoes in plaintive and mournful refrain
I see once again the towering pine trees,
And the soft rolling breadth of the plain;
I remember the small spot, secluded, alone,
Where whispering poplars and small willows stood,
By trembling grasses and nodding pink roses,
And daisies that sprinkled the heart of the wood.

MARIE JAKOBER,
Alberta

SCARFACE

Once there lived in an Indian village a young man named Scarface. He was named this because he had a big scar on his cheek and nobody liked him because of it.

One day the chief of that tribe announced that he could not find his twelve-year-old son. He said that whoever found him would marry his lovely daughter.

Scarface had always loved the girl, but he had never spoken to her because he thought she would treat him like all the rest of the people did, so he never tried to speak to her. But now he thought he'd try and look for the boy. So he started out on his quest.

He went to the village of their enemies that evening. When he arrived there, they were having a ceremonial dance. He went up to a hill and waited there until they had all gone to bed. Then he crept down quietly and went to the chief's lodge.

He stood outside and listened. He could hear somebody moaning faintly. It sounded like a little boy. He sneaked into the lodge quietly and there, tied to a pole, was the little boy. He took him down without any trouble. He put him on his back and took him out of the lodge.

Just as he was going out of the village an old woman saw him and woke some of the people in the nearby lodges with her screaming. A whole bunch of them chased after Scarface. They caught him and took him to the chief's lodge.

Scarface told the chief he had come to get the little boy. The chief told him that before he could go home with the boy he would have to do something for him. He said he would put seven skulls on the ground, and if Scarface could jump from one to the other without slipping, with the boy on his back, he would be able to go home safely with the boy. But if he couldn't do this, they would both be killed.

The chief led Scarface to the place where the skulls were. He then told him to put the boy on his back and leap from skull to skull.

Scarface bent down and pretended he was fixing the boy's shoe. While doing this he spit in two places on the ground and rubbed his feet on them. This made a thick coating of dirt on his moccasins. He then put the boy on his back and stepped on the first skull. He leaped from it to the second, and so on, without slipping.

When he had finished this he was allowed to take the boy home to his father and mother.

He took the boy home and as they were going over the hill Scarface saw somebody running to him.

As the figure came closer, he recognized it. It was the boy's sister. First she ran to her brother and kissed him, then she turned to Scarface and kissed him also.

The very next day they were happily married. They were also given a place to stay.

MARGARET TAILFEATHERS,
Alberta

THE WORKER

Have you ever seen a beaver,
  Working busily?
He builds his house and he builds his dam,
  And he does it eagerly.

Now this busy, busy beaver,
  Could to his neighbour man
Teach an important lesson;
  To work as hard as he can.

TOM PROCHER,
Ontario

LA SOURCE

En son lit moelleux de mousse gracieuse,
La source aime et caresse en route le bouleau
Et l'érable joyeux qui lui tresse un halo
Et baise tendrement la fougère onduleuse.

Le charmant rossignol prend la voix radieuse
De ce clair filet d'eau pour son propre solo
Et la brise charmée par ce doux trémolo
Fait valser mollement les ramures soyeuses.

Son cristal est si pur au soleil de midi
Que le pinson qui vient se croit au paradis
Et quand il prend son vol pour sa course légère

Son royal duvet bleu nous semble du saphir.
Le firmament joyeux, courtisant le zéphyr,
Laisse choir dans son sein son azur pour lui plaire.

ALAIN LARIVIÈRE,
Québec

EXAMINATIONS

The mere mention of examinations, in either its singular or plural form, strikes terror into the being of the pupil while bringing jubilation into that of the teacher. As it is, teachers and psychologists have attempted to explain this enigma of nature by writing books (these books occupying the better part of our libraries under the classification of Child Psychology). No doubt, this is unfair to the students of modern times whose voice, as yet, has not been heard. Therefore I defy the teachers' canes and the muddled explanations of the psychologists in now expressing our view-point.

The regular school term is a delightful and satisfying experience for the student. With scheduled chalk fights, frequent chemical explosions, and recurring detentions most of us manage to pull through the five-hour day with a smile still on our faces. As the days amble by, the teachers, now having lost all contact with the students, become more dejected. Their eyeballs begin to sink and grey hairs sprout overnight. Educationists have spent lifetimes seeking salvation for these knights of the classroom. They found the answer – Examinations!

After several months these knights are doing their best to keep on their feet. Then comes the publication of the examination schedule – not a minute too soon! The date of publication has been calculated so as to allow us little more than a week to catch up, or at least start, our work Now our hair dangles in frustration and our feet drag the corridors. These seven days pass as quickly as seven hours.

The fatal day comes. We have had nothing but seven sleepless nights to underscore seven sleepful days. Feeling that we have not been humbled enough, the teachers, with thirty minutes remaining, allow us to ask questions pertaining to the ensuing examination. No sooner has someone opened his mouth than whoof! – off they fly in a tangent. They talk about their spaniels, families, or even last summer's vacation. Explanatory drawings, slightly to the abstract, litter the board. As the period ends with their faces beaming like polished apples, they say, "Good luck students!"

The papers are passed out. Within two hours we are to write all we know (?). Some begin to write in Greek with a touch of hieroglyphics, but woe is us for our masters have graduated college with honours in languages. The questions are WORDED. They are so WORDED that none may mistake their meaning, but who understands the words? Nevertheless we must give the teachers credit; they thought this out and it is a 'Master' piece. As might be expected, the more conservative teachers work on PRINTING rather than WORDING. Letters are left out, others are smudged, and such words as Good are spelt Goude. "These are typographical errors. It's the – printing machine, you know!" Then they spend half the exam time correcting the mistakes.

On the pieces of foolscap few of us dare to add our names. "Where are those crib notes?" Nails are worn to the skin. The warden pompously paces the aisles in search of unnecessary information being passed among the inmates. The climax of the former's earnest endeavours comes when he nabs a victim and puts a big tri-coloured 'O' on his paper. Thus the week dwindles away.

Once the examinations are completed, our only hope lies in prayer. We pray that the teacher might lose his glasses, misplace our papers, or mistakingly place a 98% beside our names. These never happen. What does happen is that when the teachers correct our papers late into the night, their half-numbed brains imagine 100%'s dancing about. The subconscious takes over and our marks reach unbelievable proportions. We are saved!

As soon as the reports have completed their limited circulation, we breathe normally again. "It was nothing but a bad dream," we say, "the teachers were half asleep and so were we."

ABRAHAM HARTMAN,
Quebec

DECEMBER NIGHT

Footsteps
In the snow.
Dark, skeletal larches
Grope silently into the evening sky
By moonlight.

CORRY-ANN BARNES,
British Columbia

THE LITTLE BUSINESS MAN

Today, if you have little to do, you might come along with me to visit the little French town of Ste. Nulle Part, lying in the foothills of the Laurentian Mountains. You would not be in the least surprised, for the usual people are up and about at the usual time and doing the usual things. The baker is tantalizing the school children with his freshly-baked doughnuts; the jolly grocer is hurriedly unpacking fresh fruit; and the restaurant owner is suspiciously throwing banana peels into the boiling soup. The unusual part of Ste. Nulle Part today is, as it seems, that it is usual.

Of all the distinguished personages of this town which boasts a population of two thousand, a mayor, a policeman, and a street cleaner, the most remarkable is a little boy, Michèle. Dressed in habitant sweaters, dilapidated jeans, and weather-beaten running shoes, Michèle, the nine-year-old business man, is the pride and joy of every citizen of Ste. Nulle Part. His blond hair flows with excitement; his eyes twinkle with delight. Amiable as he appears, Michèle is a man to be feared for his hands wave dangerously whenever he talks.

It is Michèle who runs the sole paper route of *Le Journal des Hommes de la Ville de Ste. Nulle Part des Laurentides,* which is unrivalled both in title and character. Disregarding bad weather, Fridays, and holidays, *Le Journal* might be called a daily paper. Unfortunately, Michèle never has realized the necessity for both punctuality and recurrence, therefore one might excuse the ignorance of the readers of *Le Journal.*

On this morning Michèle is accompanied by his black spotted spaniel Petite. We have difficulty following these two among the time-racing pedestrians of Ste. Nulle Part. This is understandable for there is a publication today, and according to Michèle 'BUSINESS IS BUSINESS'. Michèle is recollectingly quoting figures when a bark on the part of Petite cuts him short. Approaching them are the policeman, the street cleaner, the mayor, and as many of the two thousand citizens as could congregate in five minutes. They stop in front of Michèle. Stepping forward, the mayor begins speaking in his high, squeaky voice.

"My dear Michèle, h'our city council h'as decided dat no private h'enterprise may be continued widout h-m-m widout the payment in full of de taxes h'owed to de city. In your case dat is fifty dollars."

Michèle grows pale. "But sir, mister mayor, I have not got de fifty dollars. I cannot stop my workings, for I must bring de news to the people of Ste. Nulle Part."

The people, as all wise people do, scratch their heads. Suddenly Jean the butcher shouts, "Michèle is h'our pride and joy. His paper may not h'always reach us h'on time, but he does bring *Le Journal* to Ste. Nulle Part h'anyhow. So, honourable mayor, his h'enterprise is for de public and not for de private. Derefore we, the citizens of Ste. Nulle Part, should pay his taxes."

A murmur of general consent is heard among the spectators. The mayor, for political reasons which are not to be discussed, also gives his consent. With little left to add to the debate the many citizens who had gathered in five minutes, disperse in three.

Michèle is left standing with tears in his eyes. Poor fellow! He does not know what to think. "Maybe I h'am really going bankrupt. Den I h'am a public h'enemy for I bring my paper late and h'also do not pay my taxes." Tears fall as he paces the friendless pavement. Suddenly he begins running home; he wants to run away from everybody and forget that there ever was a publication.

"WHOOF! WHOOF!" he left his secretary Petite. As Michèle stops, he apparently realizes that running away would force *Le Journal* to be filed with the holidays; it would only worsen matters. As he quickly dries his tears, the twinkle, the flow, and the cheer of Michèle return. He smiles to himself as he thinks of tomorrow's headlines: 'BUSINESS TYCOON AND SECRETARY RETURN TO HEAD OFFICE'.

ABRAHAM HARTMAN, Quebec

DESTINY

The white clouds drift like ripples out of sight;
The sea boils with the torrid heat of day;
On water, ships pursue their lonely way;
Winds whisper of the seagulls' graceful flight.
Afar the shoreline cowers, filled with fright
As angry waters splash against the sides
Of one lone ship called Destiny. It rides
The sea of life across the wake of right:
Is not this ship the cause of all our strife?
Yet we court her as drones would the queen bee;
We are as martyrs, subject to the knife,
Of this strange force that does not let us be—
For God has made a struggling death and life,
And Destiny is but the referee!

ABRAHAM HARTMAN,
Quebec

MY AMBITION

My sole ambition and unflagging desire in this world is to aid mankind in its struggle for finer things—I intend to civilize my room-mate.

I fully understand the snares and pitfalls involved in this daring project, nevertheless I shall sally forth into that unknown country, eager for conquest, yet prepared for defeats. My room-mate is somewhat of a radical. I don't mean that he is a communist; nothing so serious as that. It's just that his outlook on life is slightly twisted, due to some unfortunate incident in his childhood which has left its scar deeply engraved on his subconscious mind. The poor boy actually believes that life is meant to be enjoyed.

Evidently I must first point out to him proper school behaviour as laid down by a group of distinguished people who know what is best for school-boys. He must be taught to jump eagerly out of bed at the first tinkle of the rising bell; to trip gaily down to the washroom and complete his daily ablutions with gay abandon; to cheerfully greet his fellow searchers after knowledge at breakfast with a flashing smile; not to retire behind a smoke-screen of Pogo, football reports and the latest news, in order. In classes he must be the picture of perfect attentiveness. He must concentrate. He must banish all thoughts of football, and the girl he met last summer who had a figure that would make Marilyn Monroe jealous. He must conform.

To top this liberal education, I feel that a sprinkling of the arts would do him no harm. His taste in music is appalling. He prefers the nauseous screeching din of jazz which he describes in ecstatic joy as 'cool', 'crazy' or 'real gone', to the delicate contrapuntal harmonies of the great classical masters. His preference in literature is limited to beer ads and Micky Spillane novels. All things going well, he should be started on *The Outline of Philosophy* by the end of this term.

I believe that by constant instruction he will gradually regain his perspective, and I think deep down he will realize and thank me for it. I can tell by the way he speaks to me. Why just now he graciously enquired if I would please turn off the blessed light so that he could get some blessed sleep.

J. K. CONWAY,
Ontario

REVELATION

David stared hard at the picture. He squinched his eyes tight, swallowed hard, and stared again. The picture looked awfully angry. The long grey beard and the pointing finger. Not pointing directly at him but David had the idea that he was under direct scrutiny of that awesome object. Maybe the picture of God knew! Maybe just this minute he, David Stone, aged six, was going to be knocked cold dead because God knew!

"I can't help it, God . . . I hate Him! He's all bloody with thorns and He'll knock on the door and take me away!"

The picture hadn't changed.

David stopped and caught his breath. Where was God then? Wasn't He going to do anything? Miss Culbert at Sunday School had told him that all little boys that didn't love Jesus would end up in brimstone and fire. He didn't know what brimstone was but it sounded suspiciously like cough medicine.

The best thing to do was to find God and tell Him. But where was God? He didn't live in the parlour like Uncle Ben said. Not even under the huge dark cave of the piano. David knew, for he had looked. Looked in vain only to be laughed at by Linda. Linda with her superior smile and condescending tone as she regally informed him that he was a "wicked little heathen". Linda, tossing her head and announcing with a vague sweep of her hand that "simply everyone knew God lived there". There? Where had Linda pointed? Over that way? Yes, that was it. Right behind the south pasture to that little hill. Why, that wasn't far. Well . . . not very.

David cleared his throat and moistened his lips with his tongue. He unfolded his chubby little legs and scrambled down from the chair. It was simple. He would go to see Mr. God and tell him before anyone else did.

David looked back at the house with apprehension. Nobody was in sight. He wouldn't be gone long so nobody would miss him. Should he change his Sunday school clothes? No, they wouldn't get dirty. Besides he couldn't let God see him in short pants. He looked down in pride at his best and only pair of "longs". They would do fine.

First he would cut through the small front field and then go past the small copse of trees to the south pasture. Then it was easy. He could run across the long grassy stretch of meadow to the beckoning green hill. So David began the seemingly short and easy journey to find God.

David felt hot, grubby and tired. He peered back at the house shimmering in the heat. It looked small and far away. The little hill didn't look much closer either. Could hills walk? It seemed for every step he took forward, the hill took one backward.

"It isn't far really," he tried to convince himself. "Anyway God doesn't expect me so He won't mind if I'm late."

With this logical reasoning in mind David cheerfully hurried past the shady group of trees that separated him from the pasture. It wasn't really very far to go now. Just through the pasture and . . . the cows!

Pure terror made David stand stock still. Cows! Three of the ferocious beasts. They were eating grass and pretending not to notice him while all the time they were just waiting for a chance to chase him. He couldn't pass them by himself. It was all very well to act brave when Linda was with him, but alone! He couldn't do it.

He looked around for an escape. The long line of barbed wire stretched out on both sides of him like a skinny snake. The next field was at least half a mile away. He would have to go through this field. He couldn't walk all the way around. He had to go through this field. He parted the lowest strands of wire and wriggled under the fence.

The cows hadn't moved. He took a cautious step forward keeping a wary eye on the munching bovines. Only their jaws and their tails moved. They wouldn't bother him! A small spark of bravery flared and burst into flame. David began to walk ever so slowly toward the other side of the field. Still no response from the placid feeders. Why there was nothing to it! The silly cows didn't bother him.

A sudden movement and a heaving grunt froze him in his tracks. He turned to see a more venturesome member of the pastoral group mincing curiously toward him. For a moment the old terror washed over him. Then he ran, his short legs churning under him and his arms pumping almost as fast as his heart. Stumbling and panting he reached the welcome strands of wire and dove under them. But not without mishap. The wire was reluctant to lose such a newly won friendship and did not give up without a struggle. David won his freedom but lost the seat of his pants.

Trembling and whitefaced he picked himself up and looked back at the field. The cow was quizzically surveying him from the centre of the field. He had run all that way and torn his best pants for nothing. But at least he was on the other side.

David didn't feel very ambitious though. Just sort of shaky and tired. He sat down on a rock and contemplated crying. That was no good. He didn't even feel like crying. He felt like saying two extremely bad and wicked words.

"Damn and Hell." There! He had said them. Strange, he didn't feel any better. In fact he felt worse. He tumbled off the rock and stretched out on the warm grass. He allowed a lone self pitying tear to fall slowly off his cheek and land uncertainly on a blade of grass. He watched an inquisitive ant climb up the verdant stalk to investigate. David stared fixedly at the blade of grass and the ant. The ant had reached the tear and was nearly engulfed by it. David could not take his gaze from the tear. It seemed to magnify and grow.

The ant and the salty tear. The ant on the quivering blade of grass was on earth and so was he. He, David, with his face pressed hard against the musky smell of crushed grass was on the earth too. On earth with the ant who was nearly drowned by his tear. On earth while God was up there. Up in the sky.

David rolled over on his back and gazed intently at the sky. It looked just like a blue salad bowl upside down. How did God stay up there? Did He have swan wings like the angels? No, that couldn't be right. David reached into his pocket and pulled out the crumpled picture of God. He didn't have wings in this picture. Maybe He just used them sometimes. Maybe when He got tired of flying around He took them off and sat on a cloud till He caught His breath.

David glanced up curiously at a lone spidery cloud. What if God was up on that cloud now watching him? Up there looking down while David was here looking up. He dismissed the thought as silly. God couldn't sit on that cloud. It was too small.

David stood up eyeing the dusty road that ran across the edge of the meadow and rounded an enticing corner. A road that ran around a corner to the hill where God lived. David walked slowly over to it.

The dust on the road was warm and soft. A small breeze whirled little dust-devils on it and then rose to tease the leaves of the ash trees. David scuffed his feet, making the dust rise in small white puffs before him. It was nice on this little road, David thought as he gazed at the trees meeting and drooping overhead. Nice and shady and cool like at the bottom of a well. It was much nicer walking here than across a hot field. Maybe God built His house on this hill because He liked the trees. David decided he would ask God when he met Him. It shouldn't be much longer now, thought David. I've been walking for a long time and this road can't go much farther.

He was right. It didn't. When he rounded the next green bordered bend he stopped in amazement. So did the road, right before a tiny grey cottage with a funny roof.

Did God live here? David pushed the heavy creaking gate open with a shove and slid into the yard. Two miniature goats with black and yellow butterfly ears eyed him suspiciously and then returned to their browsing. In the corner of the yard a lady with two long grey braids was picking blackberries. David watched her small brown hands flick in and out of the tangled vines with their feathery leaves and sharp red prickles. Strong, capable hands that looked just like two brown birds flying back and forth.

David stood hesitantly on the stony walk uncertain as to what he should do. Would the lady that picked berries for God get mad at him? Perhaps he should. . . .

"Can I help you, little boy?" The lady had looked up from her work and spied David. The sound of her soft voice startled him and made him stammer.

"Please . . . I came to see Mr. God. Is He home?"

"Mr. God? . . . Home?" . . . She stared at him silently for a moment regarding him with her bright piercing eyes. Then slowly she answered.

"Why did you come here to visit God? He does not live in this house, little one."

"But . . . I . . . I . . . He must! I'm looking for Him and I can't find Him. I've got to tell Him!" David's words stumbled over each other and ended with a sob.

It was too much. The cows. His torn pants. That long, long walk. And now to find God wasn't here. David could not help himself. A large, wet tear slid down his cheek and was followed closely by another. He tried to stop them but they persisted in coming.

The lady was silent. It was such a long time since she had had a crying, confused child before her. Such a long time. She knelt down and put her strong arms around David.

"There, there, small one. Don't cry. Just tell me what is wrong."

David continued to cry. His small shoulders shaking convulsively and tears wetting his grubby little fists. Gradually he stopped, soothed by the lady's crooning voice. "She talks like she's singing," he thought. Sort of like a bird. If God didn't live here, maybe the lady knew where He lived. She might help him.

So David told the lady. He told her about Linda and Uncle

Ben, and how he couldn't find God to tell Him the terrible truth. The terrible truth that he hated Jesus. And the lady listened and wondered. Wondered how she might help this little boy.

"Why do you hate Jesus, David?"

"Because He'll come and knock on the door and take me away. Take me away and make me all thorns and blood," said David voicing his deep fear. He could see the picture of Jesus now. The picture with His eyes upward and the horrible holes and thorns in His feet. Black thorns and red. . . .

Then the lady knew what she must do. And so she began to talk. She talked and David listened while helping her pick the nubby fruit. She talked for a long time. And David listened . . . listened and wondered. There were many questions but the lady had an answer for every one of them. And so David learned. Learned about another little boy. A little boy that ran, laughed, and played. A little carpenter with no thorns. A boy that lived . . . and died. Maybe that little boy had been afraid of cows, too.

It was late afternoon when David started for home. The sunshine was nice and mellow like soft butter It looked just as David felt inside. All warm and good. The lady had mended his torn pants. Mended them so neatly that David hoped his aunt wouldn't notice that he had torn them. The lady had asked him to come back and visit her some time. David knew some time would be soon. Only one thing still bothered him. He hadn't really found out where God lived. The lady had told him that God was everywhere all the time. But David was only six years old and though he had looked wise and knowing when she told him he still didn't understand. But he did feel much better. It was nice not to hate Jesus. David wished he had known Him. He wished he could show Him how to find eggs up in the hayloft and slide down without breaking them.

The sky was so very clear that David thought he had never seen it look so high. A crow called urgently, its wings shining like tar against the sky. David had reached the cow pasture. He thought of another little boy, another little boy that wouldn't be afraid of cows. David resolved he wouldn't be afraid of them either. He entered the field slowly and even though his heart was pounding madly he suppressed the urge to run. The cows did not even deign to notice him. David would never be afraid of cows again.

David reached the cow stream and leaned against a big, rough-barked oak. It felt cool and good here. He would rest for a moment and then go home. He closed his eyes and listened. The air was warm and soft and everything sounded sleepy. The smell of sweet clover and green leaves filled the air. David opened his eyes and looked down at the brown water of the slowly moving stream. Then it happened.

A ray of sunlight grew through the protecting leaves of the huge tree until it touched the stream. A prickly excited feeling ran through David. He could not take his eyes from that light. Everything was strangely still and calm, yet he could still hear the gentle hum of insects and the slight stirring of the wind rustling the grass.

The light . . . it touched the brown water of the stream like a knife. It gleamed straight to the bottom dividing the water . . . clear, pure amber where it touched the living brown water.

David felt something grow in his throat, grow and grow until it filled his head with a wonderful choking longing. Things became so clear . . . the tree, with its tall stooping body and deep roots. David could feel the tree growing. Feel its roots deep beneath him spreading and clinging to the earth. The earth beneath him breathing and living, the air caressing and alive, and the sky above watching. Layers of life forced their way into his senses. Yet while he was acutely conscious of all these things there was only the light.

Clear and radiant it rested for a brief moment upon the stony bottom of the stream, making it gleam with a suffused glory. The light was there but a second. Then it was gone. And yet for a breathless moment David had been alive as never before, passionate for the something that eluded his understanding. He was filled with infinite longing. It was dangerous to be a human being. But in that brief instant David knew. He would never have to ask where God lived again.

IRIS HAYES,
British Columbia

L'ANGE AU CLAVECIN D'OR

La lune sautille sur le frisson des branches;
Noël s'illumine au papier peint de la crèche.
Un enfant sombre, là, le chagrin sur ses manches,
Ouvre ses yeux d'azur aux moutons et regarde,
— Bouche close —
Les rameaux alourdis de fleurs en neige rose . . .

La lune blanche au loin danse pour l'enfant sombre . . .

Là-haut, dans une étoile, un Ange aux doigts d'ivoire
Touche un clavecin d'or: — murmure dans les cordes.
L'Orient de feu souffle un Noël dans la nuit.
Noël! trille de flûte et de cloche d'or! Joie!
L'Ange au clavecin d'or chante la nuit des coeurs
— Et des pleurs — . . .

Hélas! Hélas! ne chante pas pour l'enfant sombre . . .

De son palais d'onyx, l'Ange voit les yeux purs,
La misère d'enfant: il vole sous le givre,
Module de son aile un refrain parfumé;
Pour les yeux de l'enfant, frappe une corde d'or,
L'enfant bouge son coeur et voit le rayon pâle
— De l'étoile — . . .

La ballade chante tout bas pour l'enfant sombre . . .

Il écoute: la joie fait rire son oeil clos
Et danser son chagrin: lui, fait chanter son coeur,
Rêve aux soldats de bois, aux gâteaux de miel doux,
Aux cierges flamboyants: un bonheur de Noël . . .
L'Ange, doucement, ferme son clavecin d'or . . .
— L'enfant dort — . . .

L'Ange d'amour donna son rêve à l'enfant sombre . . .

Real La Rochelle,
Québec

SPRING

Spring!
And little streams flow
In meaningless and endless journeys.
Snow melts and fades
And in its place
Spring up beautiful flowers
And small, wary, peeping blades of grass.

Jerry Hammersmith,
Saskatchewan

HOW ALBERTA CAME TO BE

Long ago water covered the sands,
The only creatures were wee tiny clams.
Then the water disappeared from dry winds,
After coming again it had fish with fins.
Again it disappeared but the land didn't dry
The swamps had animals that could fly.
After a while grew giant reptiles,
And great trees that stretched for miles and miles.
At last they were covered with mud I was told,
And to my surprise it made our coal.
The centre of the earth cooled very fast,
This made the Rockies that came to last.
It snowed and snowed which wasn't so nice,
The weight of it made solid ice.
Small and large animals then did appear,
They had hair so they didn't fear.
Then the ice disappeared leaving the land clear,
But it came back again for many a year.
This was repeated several times the books say,
But at last disappeared to leave the land as today.

There grew beautiful forests tight as mats,
Animals came like beavers and muskrats.
By some strange way the Redmen came,
And set up their teepees on the plain.
Some went south; others went east
They killed buffalo for a big feast.
Most of them settled toward the south,
Where there was food for every mouth.
The only weapons they did own,
Were bows and arrows made of stone.

The shaggy buffalo that did roam
Gave them food, clothing and a home.
Berries and meat made good food
When pounded together with tools so crude.
When the Traders came with goods to be sold,
The Indians changed – or so we are told.

ROY WESTENBERGER,
Alberta

THE POSTAGE STAMP

'Boarders Welcome'. At one time there had been a striking contrast between the brightly painted red letters and the dazzling white background of the boarding house. Those times had gone forever. Now it was difficult to distinguish the faded lettering against the dinginess of the neighbouring area. Both inside and outside, the house was badly in need of repair. Each room was furnished with only the bare necessities of life. The perpetual atmosphere of poverty and disillusionment, of hopefulness and despair, of love and fear, was almost tangible. It was an atmosphere prevalent in all the other boarding houses of downtown Toronto.

A man named Dixon occupied the downstairs room adjacent to that of the landlady. He was a typical product of this eternal emotional conflict and he looked quite at home in this dismal neighbourhood. He was a bank clerk in one of the more fashionable banks in the district. His tastes were expensive, and his budget was low.

Dixon resented his continual state of poverty and had decided to remedy the situation. His plan had been simple. He had embezzled one thousand dollars from the bank, bought stocks and bonds with it, hoping that their value would increase shortly so that he could repay the 'loan' before anyone was the wiser; at the same time, he hoped to gain a considerable amount of money. This plan was doomed to failure. The stock market did not go up and soon Dixon had spent all his money trying to redeem their value. So he decided to make a full confession of his crime and commit suicide before the contents were made public. Accordingly, he wrote a long explanatory document, enclosed the worthless bonds to atone to some extent for his sin, and went forth to post it. He placed a four cent stamp on the envelope, sealed it, and posted it. On the way back to his lodgings he bought a newspaper with his last few pennies. Once inside his room again, he drew out a revolver from the desk drawer. As he was about to press the trigger, a small article attracted his eye to the newspaper in front of him. Yes, the stocks which he had bought, had quadrupled in value. Dixon had just posted a sealed confession of his guilt, together with fifty shares, which were now worth four times their original cost.

Dixon ran downstairs and was just in time to see the six o'clock mail 'pick-up' truck disappear. In a nervous frenzy he quickly made his way to the district Post Office; it was closed for the day. He phoned the Post Office manager, and was informed that nothing could or would be done about the matter until the next morning. If he would give the employees a description of the return address on the envelope, it might be stopped. Dixon spent a fearful and restless night in his boarding house room. The Post Office doors opened promptly at eight o'clock and in stepped Dixon. He inquired as to the whereabouts of his letter immediately. Then he was told that all envelopes with business addresses had been sorted early, so that they could be delivered first. Dixon's letter would now be at the bank; he rushed there. As he entered, the manager sternly called him into his office. His heart sank; the letter had been opened. But, no! He was being congratulated for his previous good work; he was told that a substantial salary increase was in order. Try as he could during the conversation, Dixon did not catch a glimpse of his letter, even though the morning mail lay directly in front of him on the manager's desk. Feigning sickness, Dixon returned to the boarding house.

He went straight to his desk, sat down, seized the revolver and placed it to his head. Meanwhile the doorbell rang, and the postman handed the landlady a rectangular envelope. However, she assumed that Dixon was asleep, because she heard no noise from his room. She decided to deliver the letter to him later, so that he would not be disturbed. As she turned away from his room, the loud report of a revolver resounded through the building. Dixon slumped over his desk, blood pouring from the fatal wound. The newspaper which he had bought yesterday was stained crimson red. It was almost impossible for one to read an article entitled "Postage dues increase to nickel; effective to-day."

T. R. Carsley,
Ontario

THE MYSTERIOUS DOG TEAM

The wind howled across the snow swept plains of the Arctic Barren Lands. The temperature had dropped to sixty below and a real blizzard was raging outside the Brown's snug cabin.

"Oh dear," said Mrs. Brown to her husband Jake, "we're almost out of wood, you'd better go get more."

"Come on, Terry," called Jake to his oldest son who was reading by the stove, "help me pack in some wood."

Sixteen-year-old Terry rose and crossed the room to where his parka was hanging. He put it on and stepped out of his slippers into a pair of fur lined boots. Jake was already dressed so the two hurried out into the storm.

The wood pile was a few hundred yards back of the cabin. They rushed to it and each grabbed an armload of the wood.

As they started back, Terry all of a sudden heard his father yell, "Look over there!" He looked in the direction his father indicated and saw a dog sled being pulled by about eight dogs. It was soon lost to sight in the blizzard.

They went back into the house. At dinner they told the others about the dog team and they all agreed it must have been old Barry from up the creek.

Terry didn't think it was Barry but he didn't say so because he didn't have a reason for thinking otherwise.

The next morning the blizzard was over and the sun was trying desperately to shine.

Terry's six-year-old brother, Bobby, came up to him, "Will you take us out on your dog sled?" he asked.

"Okay," said Terry and the little boy ran from the room to tell nine-year-old Harry and twelve-year-old John that Terry would take them out.

"Can I go?" asked Terry's fourteen-year-old sister, Caroline. "Please," she begged as she saw Terry begin to shake his head.

"All right if you promise not to complain about the cold."

"I won't," promised his sister happily.

The youngest of the family, Susie, who was only three came running up to Terry and said, "Please, me too."

"Not this time," was the answer, "Maybe Janice will take you out for a walk." He spoke of his twin sister who was busily preparing breakfast.

Mr. Brown had left on his trapline and Mrs. Brown was sleeping.

At ten o'clock they got started off on the dog sled towards old Barry's house for Terry wanted to ask him about the mysterious dog sled.

Caroline and Bobby sat on the sled and Harry and John ran beside as Terry stood on the back.

At last they reached Barry's cabin. Terry went to the door and knocked. An old grizzled man in a dirty shirt and trousers opened the door.

"Howdy, son," he said to the boy.

"Hello, Mr. Barry," greeted Terry, "Are you feeling better now?"

"Yes, boy, yes," said the old fellow, "What can I do for you?"

"We saw a team yesterday and were wondering if it was you," answered Terry.

"In that storm? I should say not," said Mr. Barry. "It must have been one of the other trappers."

"Thank you very much, Mr. Barry," said Terry, "good-bye."

"Bye, son."

Terry returned to the others who, while they were waiting had been engaged in a snowball fight.

They resumed their ride through the snow, this time, though, Harry and John got on also.

I will take time now to tell you of the Browns. Mr. Brown was a trapper. He and his wife had lived in the barren tundra lands for the past twenty years.

All the children had been born in the very cabin that they lived in now. As they became of school age Mrs. Brown taught them all she thought necessary they should know.

It was getting dark and a light snow began to fall, making it difficult to see.

All of a sudden a dog team drawn by seven dogs shot past them. The musher neither waved nor called a greeting though the children did both, for in that isolated place few people were seen and everyone was friendly to everyone else.

"Who was it?" asked Caroline.

"I don't know," admitted Terry, "I didn't see his face but that's the team Dad and I saw yesterday. I can tell by the white lead dog."

They headed for home and reached it about six p.m. As Terry and John put the dogs in the shed where they were kept and fed them, they talked about the dog team they had seen.

"Let's try and find out who it was," suggested John eagerly. "It'll be fun."

"Okay, but I doubt if we can find out," stated Terry, "Well, let's go eat."

Terry and John set out the next morning to solve the mystery of the dog team. They had decided to go to a cave about two miles from their home. They'd thought it would be a good place to make plans. (This had been suggested by the adventurous John.)

At last they reached the cave. They halted the team and made their way into the cave.

"Look," said John, "there's a light down at the other end."

"So there is," whispered Terry, "let's go investigate."

They crept down the passage. At the end was a small crack about half an inch wide and three feet long. Over to one side of the cave was a small passageway that led into a room, that the boys could see by looking through the crack.

In the room was a long table. Around it sat eight people, seven men and a woman. Over by a stove in the corner sat another man, reading.

All around the walls were fur pelts. So many that the boys couldn't believe their eyes.

The people around the table were deep in a conversation that the boys found easy to hear.

"I passed a bunch of kids with a team yesterday," remarked one man.

"Probably was the Brown kids," said a voice that sounded strangely familiar to the boys. It was Barry!

"We'd better get these pelts into Fort Smith as soon as we can," said another man.

"We sure should, Erik," said the woman, "I want some money. After all haven't I been cooking for you guys for the past four months?"

"That's right, Josie, you and Jameson will both get your share," said Barry. He seemed to be the boss.

"What about the rest of us?" asked another man.

"Don't any of you worry about your money, you'll get it as soon as we get these furs sold," said Barry.

"It was a smart idea to steal furs from the trappers only a few at a time so they wouldn't miss them," said a man who hadn't spoken before.

Terry and John who had been listening to all this, started when they heard the last words. Terry motioned John to follow and the two slipped from the cave.

"I've got a gun here," said Terry, and he pulled a rifle from the sleigh and loaded it. "I'll hold them while you hurry back with the team and get help. Now hurry!"

John jumped on the back of the sled and started off. Terry went back into the cave cautiously.

As he came to the crack, he looked in. Everything was still the same as he'd left it.

He went right in and said, "Don't move, anyone. Just raise your hands and back up against that wall."

"Terry," said Mr. Barry, "what's going on?"

"Never mind, just do as I tell you and not a word," ordered Terry feeling very brave and yet very scared. He wasn't sure what to do.

John wouldn't be home yet and he thought that maybe Mr. Brown wouldn't be home so John would have to go all the way to Abbotts. He almost groaned at the thought.

Sophie said suddenly, "Aren't you a little young to be a policeman?"

The men laughed as Terry said, "Quiet, or I'll let you have it," the way he'd heard movie gangsters say it in the shows he'd seen in Fort Smith.

"I know you stole all these furs," said Terry. "I heard you from the cave."

"You and who else?" asked Mr. Barry, "Are the others with you?"

"I'm alone," said Terry. He didn't want them to know about John.

Suddenly a voice behind him said "Terry, I made it. Dad, Mr. Abbott and Mr. Morriss were about a quarter of a mile away with their traps. I brought them."

Terry turned; behind him stood his father and two other men. John was right behind them.

"According to the story John told us, these people have stolen furs from our traps," said Jake to Terry.

"That's right, Dad."

The eight men and Josie were taken to Fort Smith and found guilty. John and Terry were rewarded for their bravery by each getting fifty dollars. The trappers gave them the money for saving the traps.

The boys used their money to help get them out to school the next winter. They're both very grateful to 'The Mysterious Dog Team'.

FAY CALLISON,
Yukon

SHENANDOAH

Somewhere in the valley wide
In a willow by the river side
A dove laments, as on they ride
To the Shenandoah Valley.

He sees them come, yet far away
All in their glittering battle array
Comes an army from the South this day
To the Shenandoah Valley.

Some by foot, and some by steed
To fulfil their nation's need
To rid the South of Yankee greed
In the Shenandoah Valley.

Some sing praises, others thanks
Onward coming, stately ranks
Swarming down the river banks
In the Shenandoah Valley.

Bugles blare, the charge is on
In the valley thereupon
Muskets roar in the early dawn
In the Shenandoah Valley.

On they come, no ranks divide
To the foray, none subside
Shouting, firing as they ride
In the Shenandoah Valley.

Some are wounded, others die
In the battle, banners fly
Dark clouds forming in the sky
Over the Shenandoah Valley.

The South retreats with sabres bent
The cannon shattered, powder spent
Yet sings the dove with sad lament
In the Shenandoah Valley.

BOB DICKSON,
Ontario

THE HAND OF FATE

The train creaked and rattled along the track by slums, factories, streets, and people. The working day was finally over and the commuters were on their way home. Ronald White, an average office worker, was among them. There was nothing striking about Mr. White; he just blended in with the rest of the crowd. He was reading his newspaper; fighting in Malaya; conferences at Geneva; the plights of Jiggs; the welfare of a President; all these things passed before his eyes, but only evoked detached interest.

He skimmed over the Births, Marriages and Deaths page wondering if anyone he knew might be listed in one of the classifications. At the bottom of the Deaths column was a notice. "White, Ronald. At his residence on November 19, 1955. Beloved husband of Ann Black and father of Ron, Jr."

Frantically he glanced at the top of the page; the date was November 21, 1955; Ron was sure it was the fourteenth. Cautiously, he raised his head to see the date on the paper being read by the person sitting in front of him—November 14, 1955! A cold chill began to run a race with itself up and down his spine.

Ann, his wife, was waiting for him at the front door of their suburban home, and Ron Jr. came running down the stairs to greet his father; and tripped over a rug, falling flat on his face. He took it in good grace, which was surprising as he was only three years old, and picked himself up and laughed in his father's arms.

Ron was happy with his family and tried to forget the dark cloud that hung over him, but he was unable. The antics of Ron Jr. soon became boring; the dinner was insipid, the television programmes pointless.

Eight o'clock rolled around and Ron Jr. reluctantly travelled up the stairs to go to bed, followed by Ann to make sure he carried out his trust. This gave Ron time to think.

Had he been given an advance copy of the newspaper by fate to warn him of his destiny, or was it all just a practical joke played by some prankster? He decided to have a medical check-up and to remain inside the four walls of his home on Saturday.

"Nothing wrong with you," remarked the doctor, disappointed that he could not find anything to go to work on. "That'll be five dollars, please."

The week passed uneventfully for Ron. In a little crannie of his closet was wedged the newspaper in question. He did not dare look at it again, nor did he let his wife see it.

Saturday dawned bright and hopefully. The sun, at least, was happy. The same old alarm clock woke up Ron and his wife. The morning passed without incident. Maybe it was only a joke or a mistake. Ron's hopes rose.

"Would you go across the street to Mrs. Jones, and borrow some flour for me?" asked Ann, in the middle of making a cake, and having run short of the vital ingredient.

"Well, I suppose so," was the hesitant answer.

"That's a nice way to answer," retorted Ann, a little put out.

"I'm sorry, honey. Sure, I'll go. You know your wish is my command."

The door opened slowly; there was no sign of anyone or anything. Ron started across the street, a little encouraged. Suddenly, a black sedan sped out of a driveway down the street. Ron froze in his tracks with fear. He could not move; it was his destiny. There was a squeal of brakes, and then — blackness.

Several years later Ron Jr. was rummaging through his father's closet. Jammed in a corner, was an ancient newspaper, yellow, and frayed at the edges. He looked at it curiously; then threw it in the waste basket.

JOHN ROSEVEAR,
Quebec

POEM OF BEAUTIFUL WORDS

Purple, whisper, goblin, down,
Delicate, willow, tender,
Ripple, sapphire, trailing, gown,
Opal, mossy, splendour,

Shadowy, ghostly, haunting, fey,
Ivory, murmur, sea,
Island, waver, golden, ray,
Shimmer, soften, lea,

Lullaby, petal, lacy, feather,
Ether, darkness, croon,
Lovely, filmy, tranquil, heather,
Lavender, dapple, rune,

Peaceful, hearth, drowsy, fade,
Plaintive, echo, yearn,
Wind, weather, sigh, shade,
Silvery, thistle, fern.

HEAVENLY DAZE

The heavenly orchestra was practising. Not that they hadn't reached perfection already, but a final going over of the programme was needed. Violins, flutes, trombones and clarinets were carefully sounded for last minute flaws while the celebrated harpists were tuning their glorious instruments. Such great care was not usually taken for the weekly concert, but tonight was a little special. Tonight featured the best trumpet player in Paradise. The angel Gabriel had consented to render a trumpet solo and a capacity crowd was expected.

Word spread quickly among the angels. Front row clouds had gone like hot cakes and all those with more than a three-foot wing span were being politely asked to sit at the back in order not to crowd the open air theatre.

It was an hour before curtain time. Soon the rustle of feathers would announce the first arrivals. The performers awaited patiently the master Gabriel when suddenly calamity struck. A panting angel, halo awry, rushed onto the stage where holy musicians were busy setting up their racks. "Gabriel," he puffed, "can't come. He's been called for emergency earth duty!"

Blank stares followed the announcement. Mouths fell open. If ever there was despair in Heaven it was present that night. Then pandemonium broke loose.

"What will we do?"

"We've packed the house."

"Can't send them away."

"The Black Angel will never let us hear the end of this."

Then from somewhere in the wings came the only calm voice. "I", it said, "will play the trumpet for you."

Slowly the group turned their gaze to the direction of this one ray of hope. A tall, wiry angel with slightly scruffy wings and a rakish halo stood grinning from ear to ear. His bright red hair was cut in an outrageous bristle and his impudent face was covered with freckles. "Saint Peter's getting careless," whispered an angel. "This one must have sneaked in under the pearly gate."

The leader, however, was regarding him curiously. He asked the question bluntly. "*Can* you play the trumpet?"

"Yes," said the boy. "Not, of course, as well as Gabriel. But almost. In a different way."

No one lies in Heaven. The angels looked at each other. "What," they shrugged their wings, "have we got to lose?"

"Well," said the leader, "you may not be a good trumpet player, but you've got one heavenly nerve. Give it a try," and he gave the youngster a friendly pat. "However," and he caught the newcomer's eye with a stern look, "you'll be checking halos for all eternity if this is a joke."

"I'm telling you," said the precocious creature matter-of-factly, "I'm good!"

The master of ceremonies presented him with a beautiful, radiant trumpet, Gabriel's own. To his surprise the honour was declined.

"Just in case," said the angel, digging into the folds of his almost white raiment, "I brought my own," and he drew forth a battered horn. Rolling his eyes in a mute appeal for help the maestro marched grimly through the curtains and announced the substitute to the audience. A disappointed sigh swept the theatre. Angelic opinion wasn't exactly in the new angel's favour.

Peace was restored, however, during the first three numbers. The orchestra was truly magnificent and the divine audience listened intently. Then there was silence, full of apprehension for the overwrought musicians, uneasy curiosity on the part of the listeners. In the midst of the silence the young angel, standing alone, raised the horn to his lips. The first blue note broke from the trumpet and hung throbbing on the crystal air. Hauntingly lonely was the sound. Then faster and faster the notes tumbled out, sometimes tripping over each other in their haste, sometimes being sucked up by another in a long, low wail. The silence changed almost audibly. Never had Gabriel played like this. The house was enthralled. At the end of the solo the angel sat only to rise again and again as encore after encore was called for and received. When it was finished the angel, his face now one wide grin, was solemnly presented with an eternal membership in the celestial orchestra amid roaring applause.

That is why, once a month, the theatre is packed with heavenly hosts where a one-angel concert is conducted while thousands more flock the air above it. That is also the reason why, once a week at a certain time, a lean angel with a crooked halo and a flaming bush of hair is seen scurrying down the back golden streets towards Gabriel's mansion. The *back* streets because—Suffering Seraphim—Gabriel doesn't want just every spirit to know he's learning the Blues!

Lorna Drew,
Ontario

LA SCENE DU POT AU LAIT

Connaissez-vous Jules Rancourt, du petit village de Rocheblanche? Sans doute ne l'avez-vous jamais rencontré personnellement, mais regardez un peu autour de vous. . . . Vous en trouverez partout de ces petits garnements d'une dizaine d'années, à la crinière rousse mal démêlée, aux yeux espiègles au-dessus d'un nez retroussé. . . .

En plus de tous ces ornements, Jules est doté par la nature d'abondantes taches de rousseur et d'une vive intelligence. Depuis un an à peine il suit à l'école du village les savantes leçons de Mademoiselle Angéline Boislevent, et déjà le petit garçon peut lire dans les livres aussi bien que n'importe qui. Il faut ajouter aussi que Jules a la passion de la lecture. . . . Si vous ne le rencontrez pas à jouer à la balle derrière la maison des Robert, ni à dénicher les oiseaux dans le bois, ni à simuler la guerre au milieu de la rue principale, ne cherchez plus. Rendez-vous sur le bord de la gentille rivière qui coule près de Rocheblanche: là, toujours au même endroit, à l'ombre d'un chêne, vous découvrirez votre homme, plongé dans la lecture d'un livre d'aventures. . . .

Justement, en cette chaude après-midi de juin, où se trouve-t-il? Il n'est pas sur le jeu de balle où se démènent une dizaine de garçons en gilets aux couleurs claires; les oiseaux du bois ne semblent nullement dérangés dans leurs chants joyeux, et le bruit des fusils ne retentit pas dans la rue déserte. . . . Approchons-nous doucement du chêne qui se mire dans la rivière et regardons.

Ha! le voilà, notre Jules! Assis dans l'herbe, adossé à l'arbre qui l'ombrage, il semble captivé par le livre aux brillantes gravures posé sur ses genoux. Toute son attention concentrée sur ce volume, Jules ne voit pas la rivière claire qui bouillonne sur son lit de cailloux; il n'entend pas les oiseaux qui lancent dans le soleil leurs trilles audacieux; il ne sent pas le parfum enivrant qui monte de toute cette nature rajeunie caressée une douce brise. Non, Jules ne perçoit rien de tout cela. . . .

Mais, aussi, il y a de quoi! Qui ne serait intéressé par les aventures fantastiques de ce Jeannot l'aviateur? Toujours cet audacieux Jeannot est embarqué dans des aventures extraordinaires, et toujours sa force merveilleuse triomphe des événements! C'est vraiment un type épatant, cet aviateur!

Soudain, Jules ferme son livre à regret et se lève en se frottant les yeux. . . . Déjà fini, ce volume! Et juste au moment pathétique où Jeannot, forcé d'atterrir en territoire inconnu, se voit entouré par une horde féroce de sauvages aux figures d'ébène, où l'on n'aperçoit qu'une paire d'yeux blancs et deux grosses lèvres rouges! Comment le héros s'en tirera-t-il? C'est bien écrit: "A suivre la semaine prochaine", mais encore faut-il pouvoir se procurer le numéro suivant. . . . Et, par malheur, Jules a dépensé tout l'argent reçu de son père. Quant à lui demander de nouveau, il vaut mieux ne pas y songer.

Les mains dans les poches et le livre sous le bras, le gamin reprend le chemin de la maison. A peine a-t-il refermé derrière lui la porte de la demeure que sa mère lui crie de la cuisine:

"Tu n'oublieras pas d'aller chez le laitier, hein Julot?"

Ah oui! Ce fameux laitier! Tous les soirs, avant de souper, il faut aller chercher une pinte de lait chez le vendeur! Jules s'en dispenserait bien! Mais, alors, son père ne lui donnerait plus d'argent à la fin de la semaine! Et dans ce cas, adieu les livres!

A peine le temps de porter dans sa chambre le livre d'aventures, et Jules est en chemin, un pot dans une main, une pièce d'argent dans l'autre. Devant la boutique de l'épicier, tabaconiste et libraire en même temps, Jules s'arrête quelques instants pour regarder les livres à l'étalage. Justement, voici la suite des aventures de Jeannot!

Et ce volume semble encore plus intéressant que l'autre. . . . Le désir grandit dans le coeur de Jules. . . . Mais que faire?

En traversant la place publique devant la fontaine, une idée soudaine lui vient. S'il n'achetait qu'une chopine de lait et complétait avec de l'eau? Il pourrait ainsi se procurer le fameux livre. . . . Mais, n'est-ce pas un vol? . . . Probablement non, car personne ne s'en apercevrait . . . cela ne causerait de tort à personne. . . .

Jules hésite. . . . Il écoute tour à tour la voix de sa conscience et le démon qui lui souffle toutes sortes de faux prétextes. . . . Mais l'amour de la lecture l'emporte, et le garçon ne demande au laitier qu'une chopine de lait.

"Tiens, seulement une chopine aujourd'hui?" fait celui-ci, étonné.

"Oui, rien qu'une chopine," répond Jules.

A peine sorti de la boutique, il court à la fontaine dont il ouvre le robinet tout grand! L'eau s'engouffre en trombe dans le pot de lait qui déborde en éclaboussant Jules! Celui-ci retire vivement son pot; cependant, il contient maintenant plus d'eau que de lait! Jules est si pressé qu'il ne s'en aperçoit pas. Le temps de fermer le robinet, de brosser un peu son habit de la main, le voilà chez le libraire. . . .

Arrivé chez lui avec le précieux livre caché sous son gilet, Jules dépose rapidement la pinte sur la table et grimpe à toute vitesse dans sa chambre pour continuer la lecture des aventures de Jeannot l'aviateur.

Bientôt des exclamations irritées parviennent jusqu'à lui. Jules croit discerner des expressions indignées: "Ce voleur de laitier! . . . Nous verrons bien!" Puis, un appel de son père le fait descendre de sa retraite.

"Jules," dit le père, "viens avec moi chez le laitier. Regarde donc ce qu'il t'a vendu! ce n'est pas du lait, c'est de l'eau! Nous allons bien voir! Viens!"

Pauvre Jules! le voilà bien pris! Comment se tirer de ce mauvais pas? Il ne peut s'échapper. Le mieux est de faire face aux événements. . . . Tout en suivant son père chez le laitier, Jules essaie de se composer une attitude pas trop penaude. Aura-t-il la force de mentir à son père? Il vaut mieux se tenir coi le plus possible.

En arrivant chez le vendeur, M. Rancourt raconte ses griefs en accusant violemment le laitier. Mais celui-ci se défend avec indignation. Il n'a donné que du lait à Jules, du bon lait! Il ne "baptise" jamais son lait, tout le monde peut le dire! D'autre part, il n'a donné au garçon qu'une chopine de lait, comme celui-ci l'avait demandé. Même que cela l'a surpris, il a fait répéter sa demande au garçon. . . .

Alors, le soupçon naît dans l'esprit du père. Il se tourne vers son fils et lui demande:

"Comment se fait-il? Le marchand affirme t'avoir vendu une chopine seulement, et toi, tu arrives à la maison avec une pinte . . . ?"

Le pauvre garçon rougit, bredouille, puis finit par fondre en larmes. . . . Pressé par son père et le vendeur, il avoue tout, en pleurant.

Le père prend alors son fils par l'oreille et, tout en le reconduisant par les rues du village, lui dit:

"Tu vas aller reporter tout de suite ce livre au marchand. . . . Tu m'entends? Et pas d'argent pour cette semaine, monsieur le liseur. . . ."

Pauvres Jules! Il a appris à ses dépens que le vol ne rapporte pas. Et il avait à peine commencé la lecture du livre d'aventures! Il eût mieux valu attendre une semaine pour se procurer le volume! Et quelle honte quand le père raconte tout à la famille! Le malheureux garçon en a pour longtemps à être taquiné par ses frères et soeurs, sur la "scène du pot de lait", comme on l'appelle.

Je crois que, pour cette fois, Jules est guéri, et qu'il ne recommencera pas de sitôt.

PAUL BENOIT, Québec

THE PLANETS

The Planets in the blue,
To me and to you—
Are big balls of land
Beaches and sand.
Mars, Pluto and Venus,
If they could have seen us
When we were part of the sun
(Before time had begun)
Would have laughed at us
And caused great fuss.
But Mother Nature, the Nurse,
Told them, "In the universe
It doesn't matter who comes first."
Then they laughed until fit to burst.
Away from the sun as a ball of fire,
Up and up we went, higher and higher.
And all the planets watched
As in the sun we notched
A great hole in its side,
Then the planets began to hide,
And that is where they stay
To this very day.

CHARLES R. EISENER,
Nova Scotia

THE STORM

Small
Black cloud.
A few drops fall.
The thunder rumbles loud.
The torrent beats upon the earth
With unrestrainèd violence which no force
In earth or hell can curb. There is no mirth
In this. It ravages with no remorse.
The deluge slackens in the light.
The thunder growls afar.
The breeze is light.
Clouds are
White.

RONALD VINCE,
Ontario

A FABLE?

It was indeed a great day!

For the first time in all history the animals of the world were to unite into one great nation—the United Animals. No longer would they follow the philosophy of kill or be killed. No longer would the carnivora prey upon the herbivora. Instead, they would unite into one vast, glorious nation of equals, a nation that would rise to unparalleled heights of democracy and glory!

The first day they celebrated. The second and third days were spent in resuscitation. On the fourth day they began the work.

The legislative branch of the government was confronted by a disconcerting number of complex problems, requiring a maximum of tact and ingenuity, which everyone agreed they possessed.

The first desideratum was a national anthem.

One faction wanted the anthem to be 'O Animal-land'. The other wanted 'God Save Animal-Land'. Faced with the alarming prospect of no anthem to open this session of Parliament – which was unthinkable – the members made a desperate compromise and selected 'The Leaves and Grass Forever'.

A second enigma, closely akin to the first, was a national flag.

"Why have a national flag? Why don't we keep the symbol we've always had, one we've lived under all our lives – a green leaf?" one member half-belligerently, half-timorously asked.

The House rocked with laughter. "No flag? Who ever heard of a country with no national flag?"

And therefore, the conservatives – the 'old guard' – submitted their design, a tree with green leaves, green grass growing about it, a blue sky overhead, and a white background. The more progressive members supported a flag of less conventional design. It was a – that is to say it resembled a – or rather one might say it was – although it actually seemed. . . . Perhaps I should give my interpretation. Its background was a conservative crimson. From the top, flowing to the centre, were myriad streams of green, terminating in one bold blue sweep, right to the bottom. And in one corner, with a purple head, sat a leering nude.

When the work was unveiled in the House, the gallery gasped, the Speaker gave an agonized squeak, and four chipmunks fainted. Immediately the President ordered the flag removed, on the grounds that it was objectionable, and half-fainting, red-faced officials scurried over and quickly hid the offending object. Needless to say, the House chose the initial entry.

The third problem was one of subversion.

A representative from the mid-west said, with passionate patriotism, "We've had twenty thousand years of treason! This conspiracy is threatening to undermine our Animal-way-of-life. We've got to take a firm stand and stop coddling them. Our country is full of subversives. It's time someone cleaned up this mess."

Parliament, taking his advice, passed by an overwhelming majority a law making it a crime for an animal to know a human being, to belong to any organization dealing with human beings, to associate with anyone associating with human beings, and to read any literature written by a human.

The junior representative, who had shown so much patriotic zeal, was made chairman of a sub-committee, and was soon exposing subversives in every walk of life. He no doubt would have accomplished more for the security of the country, but for the discovery that a cousin of his, four times removed, had married a French poodle, property of one Marilyn Monroe. The junior representative was, of course, immediately removed from his position and sentenced to five years hard labour, i.e., starching stuffed shirts.

There were many other issues debated, but most of them were rather dull and not worth noting.

However, about two weeks after that great day of unity, a first hint of dissension appeared.

A bear, who had been appointed Commander-in-Chief of the army, was on a banana diet. Why it had been decided that he should eat bananas no one knew. But the fact remained that he ate bananas. At first he enjoyed them. However, after two weeks of only bananas, he began to complain. And one day something happened that was the last straw.

The bear awoke to find the monkey, who had been assigned to peeling the bananas for him, gone. Heeding the gnawing in his stomach, the bear took a banana and attempted to peel it. On his first attempt he held it too tightly and mangled it rather badly. On his second attempt the result was the same. The third, fourth, and fifth attempts produced the same mangled mass. At this point, the bear quite lost his temper. With a roar of rage, he charged blindly at the mound of bananas, jumped up and down on it with sadistic viciousness, and finally, as a climax, sat on it. He then turned and waddled into the forest in search of more substantial fare, and growled something about 'crazy ideas'.

Then the wolves, tired of eating chopped-grass-root roasts, deserted.

The foxes went into the forest one day, and several hours later staggered back, tongues hanging out, eyes glazed, grinning vacuously, and giggling at the slightest provocation. Apparently they had found some over-ripe grapes.

One by one the carnivora left, until none remained. Only through the efforts of the President were the other animals persuaded to stay, and most reluctantly, for it was rumoured that all the carnivora had gathered in the forest and were planning something.

One day, Hamish the hare, President of the Republic, had attempted to overtake a group of animals that had slipped off. Failing to find them, he was returning to the city when he heard a noise. As he neared the city it grew louder and louder until he could see what was causing it.

All the animals—deer, mice, rabbits, squirrels, and the rest—dashed by, screaming in terror. Behind them, with greedy jaws agape, bounded the carnivora.

Hamish hopped toward them as fast as he could. Then, seeing the old wolf, Leopold, directing the attack, he spluttered, "Stop it! Stop it at once, do you hear?"

The old wolf whirled about with a snarl. Seeing Hamish he stopped, uncertain.

"I say, you've got to stop this, immediately!"

The wolf remained silent.

"Did you hear me? I said you've got to stop this. You've no right to do this. You know it's against the law."

The wolf did not reply, but slowly advanced. The rabbit began to retreat, his eyes filling with fear. But before he could turn to run, the wolf, with one great leap, knocked him down and quickly ate him.

Then, having finished, the old wolf looked up slowly at the fleeing animals and reflected, "You know, Hamish, you were right." A new thought struck him. He smiled a sly, greedy satisfied smile, and said softly, "But I was bigger."

PETER YURKIW,
Ontario

ECHOES OF SIGHT

Mist hanging low over the mountain tops
like a drifting, fluffy cloud,
engulfing them like angel hair.

Cold, blue cascades, tumbling, falling,
screaming down steep mountain cliffs
and crevices.

Stark, barren, rocky forms bordered by
leafless, charred remnants of a
cursed spark.

The old, empty, battered shacks, high in the
hills, beside the brook, filled with
trout, where once a tired, dirty
logger sheltered.

And the muddy river, twisting, turning,
through jagged shoreline downward
to the sparkling sea.

GARRICK HAGON,
Ontario

TO A PRINCESS OF THE ESTE FAMILY

Her hair was gold upon her head,
Tied with a cord of silvery thread,
Held with a pearl encrusted comb,
And, woven round into a dome,
It glistened.

Her cheeks had been brushed with a soft pink light,
But the rest of her face was milky white
Except her lips which were crimson red—
A gash of colour 'gainst the rest of her head,
As she smiled.

Her eyes were palely glowing blue
Like star-grass in the meadow spread with dew:
Darkly fringed above and under,
Framed by a gentle brow expressing wonder
As she listened.

Her dress was a heavy satiny rose
Embroidered with crystal beads in rows.
And, tied with a wide green sash,
It matched the green above her lash.
She glowed.

Susan Hallett,
Quebec

GONE LITTLE TOKYO

A gust of the dull smoked-filled air touched my face as I walked down familiar Powell Street in Vancouver. I returned gladly last August expecting it to be the same as prior to the evacuation. But memories were there, faint at first; familiar aged structures, forlorn and lifeless streets. Where was the gaiety and romance which the Isei and the Neisei both cherished? Where were the carefree days my mother used to talk about? Only in memory I saw the former shops and sobayas which once were a famous rendezvous.

I was a stranger. From somewhere out of a dark corner came the voice of a drunk staggering and cursing in a meaningless vulgarism. This was the street I used to walk with my parents. This was the street where we used to play hop-scotch. Somewhere behind me a slow moving Chinese stared at me disinterested. Or a hearty voice called "Hi, stranger". I stared unknowingly. Where were the Japanese to welcome me with outstretched arms? In a moment I recollected all the pleasant scenes of my childhood. It was then I realized: Powell Street was dead, it would never rise again.

As I walked through the worn out streets my shoes echoing on the sidewalk; gone was the beat, gone was the rhythm, and gone was the heart of Little Tokyo that would linger forever in my mind — a thriving community that merely existed on borrowed time.

MICH TOYOTA,
British Columbia

IN THE GARDEN

While walking with my father
I look a little small,
But while I'm in the garden
I look quite tall;
For all the bees and butterflies,
And blackbirds on the wall,
Must think that I'm a giant
If they can think at all.

ERNEST MILLICHAMP,
Quebec

COUSINS

Yes, we're cousins,
My cousin and I.

We quarrel and fight,
We scratch and bite;
But after a while
We smile.

They say we are like one
In study and in fun.
Which one is which?
Some will ask.
To answer the question
Is an easy task.

You see, we're cousins,
My cousin and I.

GRACE KRYWULAK,
Saskatchewan

LINES COMPOSED WHILE GAZING THOUGHTFULLY AT THE SUNSET OUT OF THE PARTIALLY-OPENED WINDOW OF AN OVERCROWDED BUS PROCEEDING WESTWARD ALONG NO. 2 HIGHWAY

Earth has not anything to show more fair:
Dull would he be of soul who could pass by
—*Kindly remove your elbow from my eye* . . .
This City now doth like a garment wear
—*Sir, stop dripping ice cream on my hair!*
Get off my ribs, you! Someone's gonna die . . . .
Open unto the fields,—*Why must you lie*
Across my backbone? Someone tell me where
My left leg went to?—Now my foot's asleep!! . . .
In his first splendour valley,—*Ouch!* —or hill;
Ne'er saw I, never felt, a calm so deep! . . .
Hey! Close that window! Want to get a chill?
I feel a hand towards my wallet creep—
And all that mighty heart is lying still!

SANDY LEGGATT,
Ontario

NOTES ON CONTRIBUTORS

The ages and grades given apply to the time when the work was written

Abella, Jackie M.: Age 17; Harbord Collegiate Institute, Toronto, Ontario; Grade XII. Author of *The End Of The Story*, p.42.

Adams, Maria: Age 17; Moncton High School, Moncton, New Brunswick; Grade XI. Author of *The Snowflake*, p.138.

Amaron, Robert: Age 17; Stanstead College, Stanstead, Quebec; Grade XII. Author of *Alone*, p.135.

Anderson, Betty: Age 16; South Porcupine High School, South Porcupine, Ontario; Grade XII. Author of *The Stranger*, p.102.

Axford, Barry: Age 13; Gray School, Gray, Saskatchewan; Grade VIII. Author of *Our Farm*, p.103.

Bahrich, Mary: Age 18; Bedford Road Collegiate Institute, Saskatoon, Saskatchewan; Grade XII. Author of *On Handshakes*, p.95.

Barbour, Joe: Age 15; St. Michael's School, St. John's, Newfoundland; Grade X. Author of *Incident On The Bus*, p.24.

Barcelo, Michel: Age 17; Collège Jean de Brébeuf, Montreal, Québec; Grade Philosophie, 2. Author of *La Cité des Hommes*, p.96.

Barnes, Corry-Ann: Age 16; Stanley Humphries High School, Castelgar, British Columbia; Grade XI. Author of *December Night*, p.162.

Bartlett, Martin: Age 16; King Edward High School, Vancouver, British Columbia; Grade XII. Author of *Prologue & Epilogue*, p.27; *Elegy*, p.36.

Begor, Anne C.: Age 14; Trafalgar School for Girls, Montreal, Quebec; Grade IX. Author of *The Trail*, p.77; *Night Wind*, p.55.

Bell, Edward P.: Age 14; McAdam Composite School, McAdam, New Brunswick; Grade IX. Author of *The Canadian Field*, p.142.

Benoit, Paul: Age 15; Séminaire de Québec, Québec; Grade X. Author of *La Scene du Pot Au Lait*, p.191.

Bray, Handa: Age 15; Hudson High School, Hudson, Quebec; Grade XI. Author of *Star Gazing*, p.5.

Buchanan, Shirley Anne: Age 15; Baddeck Rural High School, Indian Brook, Victoria County, Nova Scotia; Grade X. Author of *Autumn Rain*, p.10.

Burritt, Lloyd Edmund: Age 13; Elphinstone Junior-Senior High School, Gibsons, British Columbia; Grade VIII. Author of *Winter Fantasy*, p.41.

Callison, Fay: Age 13; Dawson Elementary-High School, Dawson City, Yukon; Grade IX. Author of *The Mysterious Dog Team*, p.179.

Carsley, Timothy Ross: Age 17; Trinity College School, Port Hope, Ontario; Grade XIII. Author of *The Postage Stamp*, p.177.

Conway, Abbott Jr.: Age 14; Huntsville High School, Huntsville, Ontario; Grade IX. Author of *My Waterfall*, p.117.

CONWAY, JEROME KENNETH: Age 17; St. Andrew's College, Aurora, Ontario; Grade XIII. Author of *My Ambition,* p.165

CORRIGAN, DIANE: Age 15; Welland High and Vocational School, Welland, Ontario; Grade XIII. Author of *The Little Fir Tree's Story,* p.73; *A Conversation,* p.74.

CRANSTON, WAYNE: Age 16; Central Collegiate Institute, London, Ontario; Grade XI. Author of *It Can't Happen Here,* p.99.

CREIGHTON, CYNTHIA: Age 14½; Bishop Strachan School, Toronto, Ontario; Grade XI. Author of *Night,* p.133.

DICKSON, BOB: Age 18; Sir Adam Beck Collegiate, London, Ontario; Grade XI. Author of *Shenandoah,* p.184.

DREW, LORNA: Age 17; Collegiate and Vocational Institute, Kirkland Lake, Ontario; Grade XII. Author of *Poem of Beautiful Words; Heavenly Daze,* p.188.

EAGLESPEAKER, SHIRLEY: Age 16; Cardston High School, Cardston, Alberta; Grade X. Author of *The Sundance,* p.7.

EARLE, GARY: Age 18; Delhi District High School, Delhi, Ontario; Grade XIII. Author of *Guess What?* p.148.

EARLE, JUDY: Age 17; Runnymede Collegiate Institute, Toronto, Ontario; Grade XII. Author of *Speed,* p.147.

EBACHER, ROGER: Age 19; Séminaire d'Amos, Abitibi, Québec; Grade Philosophie, 1. Author of *Mai,* p.118.

EISENER, CHARLES R.: Age 13; Admiral Westphal School, Dartmouth, Nova Scotia; Grade VIII-A. Author of *The Planets,* p.195.

FATT, FAY WEASEL: Age 17; Cardston High School, Cardston, Alberta; Grade X. Author of *Time Of Prayer,* p.9.

FINDLAY, VALERIE JOAN: Age 15; Weston Collegiate and Vocational School, Weston, Ontario; Grade X. Author of *Wendigo,* p.44.

FRECKER, HELENA: Age 16; Mercy College, St. John's, Newfoundland; Grade X. Author of *Newfoundland Spring,* p.37.

FRENCH, DAVID BENSON: Age 16; Harbord Collegiate Institute, Toronto, Ontario; Grade XI. Author of *A Day Of Hookey,* p.58.

FRY, DALE SHARON: Age 15; Dawson Elementary-High School, Dawson City, Yukon; Grade XI. Author of *The Northern Lights,* p.44.

GARON, JEAN: Age 17; Collège des Jésuits de Québec, Québec; Grade Rhétorique. Author of *Eclairs,* p.56.

GATES, MARION: Age 16; Port Williams School, Port Williams, Nova Scotia; Grade XI. Author of *Autumn,* p.112; *My Dream Ship* and *Nature's Work,* p.113.

GATES, WENDY M.: Age 13; Dunnville High School, Dunnville, Ontario; Grade IX. Author of *Winter Etching,* p.29.

GILLIS, RYAN: Age 14; Rocky Mountain House High School, Rocky Mountain House, Alberta; Grade X. Author of *The Mountain Goat,* p.126.

GRANT, JOHN A. G.: Age 14; Kapuskasing High School, Kapuskasing, Ontario; Grade XI. Author of *Civilization,* p.35.

GRESCOE, PAUL: Age 15; St. Paul's College, Winnipeg, Manitoba; Grade XI. Author of *Winnipeg,* p.21; *Elm,* p.63.

GRIFFITHS, FRANCES W.: Age 16; Markham District High School, Markham, Ontario; Grade XII. Author of *Final Assignment,* p.90.

GROSKORTH, PAUL: Age 17; Wingham District High School, Wingham, Ontario; Grade XII. Author of *Touching,* p.34.

HAGON, GARRICK: Age 16; University of Toronto Schools, Toronto, Ontario; Grade XI. Author of *Echoes Of Sight,* p.200.

HALDENBY, CHARLOTTE G.: Age 12; Dawson Public School, Dawson City, Yukon; Grade VIII. Author of *My Pal And I,* p.89; *An Odorous Experience,* p.51.

HALLETT, SUSAN: Age 16; Trafalgar School for Girls, Montreal, Quebec; Grade XI. Author of *To A Princess Of The Este Family,* p.201.

HAMMERSMITH, JERRY: Age 16; Melfort Composite Collegiate, Melfort, Saskatchewan; Grade XII. Author of *Spring,* p.175.

HARDING, WAYNE ROGER: Age 16; Woodfibre Elementary-Senior High School, Woodfibre, British Columbia; Grade XI. Author of *Sukanen,* p.2.

HARTMAN, ABRAHAM: Age 16; Westhill High School, Montreal, Quebec; Grade XI. Author of *Examinations,* p.160; *Destiny,* p.165; *The Little Business Man,* p.163.

HAYES, IRIS: Age 17; Richmond High School, Richmond, British Columbia; Grade XII. Author of *Revelation,* p.167.

HAYMAN, MARSHA: Age 13; Comox Elementary School, Comox, Vancouver Island, B.C.; Grade VIII. Author of *Present Day Pioneers,* p.65.

INGRAM, ANDREE M.: Age 16; Burnaby South High School, South Burnaby, B.C.; Grade XII. Author of *Grey Morning,* p.62.

JAKOBER, MARIE: Age 14; Correspondence School, Fairview, Alberta; Grade VIII. Author of *The Hidden Grave,* p.156.

JOHNSON, ROSEMARY: Age 13; General Wolfe School, Winnipeg, Manitoba; Grade VIII. Author of *Big Decision,* p.11.

JONCAS, MARC: Age 20; Collège Jean de Brébeuf, Montreal, Québec; Grade Philosophie, 1. Author of *L'Aurore de Pierre,* p.1.

KADONAGA, S. JAMES: Age 17; Delta Secondary School, Hamilton, Ontario; Grade XII. Author of *On Taking Home The Report,* p.71.

KATZ, KAROL: Age 15; Baron Byng High School, Montreal, Quebec; Grade X. Author of *A Storm,* p.120.

KENDALL, GAIL ANN: Age 12; Douglas Road Junior High School, North Burnaby, British Columbia; Grade VII. Author of *The Legend Of The Thunderbird,* p.114.

KOLODINSKI, ELSIE: Age 17; Thorhild High School, Thorhild, Alberta; Grade XII. Author of *Listen, Ye Sons Of Alberta!* p.106.

KRYGSVELD, DAVID: Age 14; Como Lake High School, New Westminster, British Columbia; Grade IX. Author of *Vacations Unlimited,* p.20.

KRYWULAK, GRACE: Age 15; Ituna High School, Ituna, Saskatchewan; Grade X. Author of *Cousins,* p.203.

LACEY, EDWARD: Age 13; Lindsay Collegiate Institute, Lindsay, Ontario; Grade IX. Author of *Snowflakes; The Tiger,* p.127.

LAIDLAW, WILLIAM (BILL) G.: Age 19; Wingham District High School, Wingham, Ontario; Grade XIII. Author of *The Floods Came,* p.155.

LANDSBERG, MICHELE: Age 16; Earl Haig Collegiate Institute, Toronto, Ontario; Grade XII. Author of *Gypsy's Dance, Revisited, Mood,* p.128; *Departure, Incongruity,* p.129.

LARIVIERE, ALAIN: Age 16; Séminaire St. Jean d'Iberville, St. Jean, Québec; Grade: Belles Lettres. Author of *La Source,* p.160.

LA ROCHELLE, REAL: Age 18; Séminaire d'Amos, Abitibi, Québec; Grade: Belles Lettres. Author of *L'Ange Au Clavecin D'Or,* p.174.

LEE, DENNIS: Age 16; University of Toronto Schools, Toronto, Ontario; Grade XII. Author of *Free Verse,* p.26.

LEGGATT, ALEXANDER (SANDY) M.: Age 14; Oakville Trafalgar High School, Oakville, Ontario; Grade X. Author of *Lines Composed,* p.204.

LEVYTSKY, YARKO: Age 18; Harbord Collegiate Institute, Toronto, Ontario; Grade XII. Author of *The Mouth Organ,* p.140.

LYTLE, CLIVE: Age 16; Como Lake Junior High School, New Westminster, British Columbia; Grade XII. Author of *So Young, So Brave,* p.144.

McGIRR, MARIAN: Age 14; Central Collegiate Institute, Regina, Saskatchewan; Grade IX. Author of *The Day Regina Blew Down,* p.53.

McKENZIE, DELPHINE: Age 13; Elementary Correspondence School, New Westminster, B.C.; Grade VIII. Author of *Red White and Blue,* p.97.

McLAREN, DUNCAN: Age 16; Hillfield High School, Hamilton, Ontario; Grade XII. Author of *How To Win Marks And Influence Masters,* p.38.

MACRAE, ALLAN: Age 17; Crescent Heights High School, Calgary, Alberta; Grade XII. Author of *A Liberal-Minded Person,* p.91.

MARLEAU, ANNETTE: Age 17; Elphinstone Junior-Senior High School, Gibsons, B.C.; Grade XII. Author of *On Literary Works,* p.100.

MARSDEN, LA ROY: Age 16; Cardston High School, Cardston, Alberta; Grade X. Author of *Daydreaming,* p.133.

MELVILLE, ROBERT: Age 17; Pickering College, Newmarket, Ontario; Grade XII. Author of *The Ditch,* p.11.

MILLICHAMP, ERNEST: Age 14; Chambly County High School, St. Lambert, Quebec; Grade VII. Author of *In The Garden,* p.203.

MONK, EILEEN: Age 17; Enderby Junior-Senior High School, Grindrod, British Columbia; Grade XII. Author of *Sonnet,* p.121.

MORRIS, JANET: Age 16; St. Joseph's High School, Grande Prairie, Alberta; Grade XII. Author of *To A Wild Horse,* p.71.

MORTON, JOANNE: Age 15; Miles Macdonell Collegiate, East Kildonan, Manitoba; Grade X. Author of *Nature's Call,* p.25.

MOSS, DORIS: Age 14; Hunt Memorial Academy, Gander, Newfoundland; Grade X. Author of *The Hunted,* p.94.

MULLALLY, PEGGY: Age 17; Souris High School, Souris, Prince Edward Island; Grade XII. Author of *Rich Uncles,* p.19.

PARHAM, PHYLLIS: Age 16; Chambly County High School, St. Lambert, Quebec; Grade XI. Author of *The Sea At Dawn,* p.108.

PARSONS, DAVID J.: Age 16; Upper Canada College, Toronto, Ontario; Grade X. Author of *A Warrior's Return,* p.80.

PATTON, GAIL: Age 16; Port Credit High School, Port Credit, Ontario; Grade XI. Author of *Our English Language,* p.96.

PERRY, DAVID B.: Age 15; Pickering District High School, Pickering, Ontario; Grade XI-B. Author of *Free Fall,* p.46.

PETRIE, ALLAN: Age 15; Bedford Road Collegiate, Saskatoon, Saskatchewan; Grade X. Author of *Winter Road,* p.7.

PIKE, GRACE: Age 13; St. Michael's School, St. John's, Newfoundland; Grade VIII. Author of *My Grandpa,* p.5.

PLOURDE, REMI: Age 15; Séminaire de Chicoutimi, St. Jerome, Lac St. Jean, Québec; Grade: Versification. Author of *Partie De Pêche,* p.76.

POLEY, KAREN L.: Age 16; New Richmond Consolidated School, New Richmond, Quebec; Grade XI. Author of *The Forsaken,* p.150.

PROCHER, TOM: Age 15; York Memorial Collegiate, Toronto, Ontario; Grade X. Author of *The Worker,* p.159.

PULLEN, JOYCE: Age 16; Brooks High School, Powell River, British Columbia; Grade XI. Author of *The Frog,* p.40.

QUINTON, DAVID: Age 17; St. Michael's School, St. John's, Newfoundland; Grade XI. Author of *Too Much Turkey,* p.152.

RALLIS, NICHOLAS (NICK): Age 18; East York Collegiate, Toronto, Ontario; Grade X. Author of *God's Country,* p.65.

RIDEOUT, GORDON HAROLD: Age 17; Ingonish Beach Consolidated School, Ingonish Beach, Nova Scotia; Grade XI. Author of *Dawning,* p.33.

ROBERTSON, MARILYN: Age 17; Burnaby South High School, South Burnaby, British Columbia; Grade XII. Author of *Fog,* p.148.

ROBINSON, PATRICIA: Age 16; Westdale Secondary School, Hamilton, Ontario; Grade XIII. Author of *Autumn's Age,* p.151.

ROSEN, BEVERLEY ANN: Age 16; West Glen High School, Edmonton, Alberta; Grade XI. Author of *Twisted Roots,* p.82.

ROSEVEAR, JOHN G.: Age 15; Montreal West High School, Montreal, Quebec; Grade XI. Author of *The Hand Of Fate,* p.186.

ROUSSEAU, SERGE: Age 18; Collège Jean de Brébeuf, Montreal, Québec; Grade: Philosophie, 1. Author of *On Ne Joue Plus Bach Au Ciel!* p.30.

RYRIE, ANNE: Age 17; Runnymede Collegiate Institute, Toronto, Ontario; Grade XIII. Author of *My Grandfather,* p.22.

SABIA, MAUREEN J.: Age 14; St. Catharines Collegiate and Vocational School, St. Catharines, Ontario; Grade IX. Author of *On Being A Doctor's Daughter,* p.104.

SAWATSKY, MERLE M.: Age 14; Humboldt Collegiate Institute, Humboldt, Saskatchewan; Grade IX. Author of *Lace; May Moon,* p.50.

SLINN, GEORGE: Age 17; Elphinstone Junior-Senior High School, Gibsons, British Columbia; Grade XII. Author of *English Forty,* p.52.

SMITH, NANCY JANE: Age 15; Mount Royal High School, Montreal, Quebec; Grade XI. Author of *A Canadian Heroine,* p.93.

STEIN, DAVID LEWIS: Age 19; Forest Hill Collegiate, Toronto, Ontario; Grade XIII. Author of *Two Poems,* p.18.

SULLIVAN, LILY: Age 15; St. Bride's College, Littledale, St. John's, Newfoundland; Grade XI. Author of *Newfoundland Name-Lore,* p.110.

SYROID, MARY C.: Age 17; Spedden School, Vilna, Alberta; Grade XI. Author of *The Robin,* p.109.

TAILFEATHERS, MARGARET: Age 16; Cardston High School, Cardston, Alberta; Grade X. Author of *Scarface,* p.158.

TAMO, LOVIE: Age 14; Western Technical and Commercial School, Toronto, Ontario; Grade IX. Author of *Rescued,* p.34.

TAMPLIN, MORGAN JOHN: Age 15; North Toronto Collegiate, Toronto, Ontario; Grade XI. Author of *The Voice,* p.130.

TASCHEREAU, JACQUELINE: Age 12; Sacred Heart Convent, Halifax, Nova Scotia; Grade VIII. Author of *The Pet Giraffe,* p.52.

TOYOTA, MICH: Age 18; Penticton High School, Penticton, British Columbia; Grade XIII. Author of *Gone Little Tokyo,* p.202.

VAN LOAN, PAUL R.: Age 18; Jarvis Collegiate Institute, Toronto, Ontario; Grade XIII. Author of *Night,* p.49.

VINCE, RONALD: Age 18; Waterford High School, Waterford, Ontario; Grade XIII. Author of *The Storm,* p.196; *Double, Double,* p.122.

WAGSTAFFE, FRANCES: Age 16; Correspondence School, Vennachar, Ontario; Grade X. Author of *Dew-Drops,* p.138.

WENSEL, EDWARD: Age 15; Armena High School, Armena, Alberta; Grade X. Author of *Farm To The Finish,* p.136.

WESTENBERGER, ROY: Age 12; Acadia Valley School, Acadia Valley, Alberta; Grade VII. Author of *How Alberta Came To Be,* p.176.

WEYMAN, WENDY: Age 16; Oakville Trafalgar High School, Oakville, Ontario; Grade XI. Author of *The Fishpond,* p.39.

WHITMAN, JEAN: Age 17; Lawrencetown High School, Lawrencetown, Annapolis County, Nova Scotia; Grade XI. Author of *Making A Dime Go A Long Way,* p.28.

WILSON, FRAN: Age 18; Linwell Thorold High School, Thorold, Ontario; Grade XIII. Author of *November,* p.119.

WILSON, PHIL: Age 18; Vancouver Technical Junior-Senior High School, Vancouver, British Columbia; Grade XII. Author of *Lament For A Can Of Salmon,* p.92.

WRIGHT, E. GERALD V.: Age 15; Hillfield School, Hamilton, Ontario; Grade IX. Author of *A Shropshire Experience,* p.78.

WRIGHT, SHIRLEY: Age 17; Chilliwack Senior High School, Chilliwack, British Columbia; Grade XII. Author of *Silence Songs,* p.139.

WYLIE, DONALD ARTHUR: Age 19; Albert College, Belleville, Ontario; Grade XIII. Author of *Black Hours,* p.63.

YURKIW, PETER: Age 17; Runnymede Collegiate Institute, Toronto, Ontario; Grade XII. Author of *A Fable,* p.196.

ZUK, JERRY: Age 17; Miles Macdonell Collegiate Institute, Winnipeg, Manitoba; Grade XI. Author of *Night And The Veldt,* p.120.